Introduction

The Science Coordination Group was set up with the aim of producing
specialised revision material for National Curriculum Science.
This is one of a set of six Workbooks which provide a full course of
tailor-made questions ideally suited to all the main Exam Board syllabuses for
GCSE Double Science.

These Workbooks have been produced to complement the popular range of
Revision Guides produced by the Science Coordination Group for GCSE
Double Science.

Throughout these books there is constant emphasis on the inescapable
need to _**keep learning the basic facts**_. This simple message is hammered home
without compromise and without remorse, and whilst this traditionally brutal
philosophy may not be quite in line with some other approaches to education,
we still rather like it.   But only because it works.

Published by Coordination Group Publications
Typesetting and layout by The Science Coordination Group

Coordinated by Paddy Gannon BSc MA

Contributors
Dr Nigel Saunders
Carol Graves
Christopher Christofi

With thanks to Colin Wells for the proof-reading

Printed by Hindson Print, Newcastle upon Tyne.

Contents

Biology Apparatus

The Basic Apparatus

1) This is a set of apparatus used in many Biological experiments.

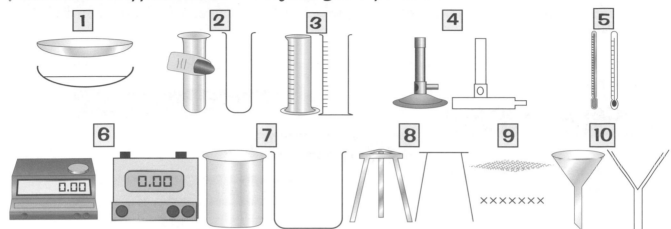

Complete the table by naming the apparatus and stating its main function.
One has already been done for you.

	Name of apparatus	Main function
1		
2	E.g. Boiling tube	Used to heat solutions.
3		
4		
5		
6		
7		
8		
9		
10		

2) Match the apparatus (heads) to its correct use (tails).

Apparatus   Use

a) Microscope   Spinning a sample to separate it into its constituents.

b) Scalpel   To inject or extract specific quantities of a fluid.

c) Pestle and mortar   Preparation of hard brittle substance for analysis.

d) Syringe   To examine a subject using large and small magnifications.

e) Mounting needle   Measure the weight of a substance to a high level of accuracy.

f) pH probe   To position a subject so that it is suitable to
                           be examined or experimented with.

g) Top pan balance   To detect the acidity or alkalinity of a substance.

h) Centrifuge   To dissect an organ with a clean incision.

Top Tips:
All this is pretty basic stuff — you'll know the names and uses of all these pieces of apparatus by now. In your investigation work, you need to show that you can make accurate observations and measurements to collect reliable evidence — and you need to know *which* apparatus would be *most useful* for a particular task.

Biology Apparatus

Choosing the Correct Apparatus

1) *It is important to choose the correct apparatus for the job. For example, measuring a certain volume of liquid in different situations requires a different degree of precison and therefore different apparatus.*

Look at the following situations and choose the most appropriate piece of apparatus for the job from the list given.

$10cm^3$ measuring cylinder

$100cm^3$ measuring cylinder

$50cm^3$ measuring cylinder

$250cm^3$ beaker

$25cm^3$ graduated pipette

a) Measuring exactly $8cm^3$ of hydrochloric acid.
b) Measuring exactly $30cm^3$ of water.
c) Measuring $200cm^3$ as accurately as possible.
d) Measuring $200cm^3$ of water which will go in a water bath.
e) Measuring exactly $25cm^3$ of sodium hydroxide.

Dangers with Apparatus

2) Match up the *situation* (*Heads*) with the *correct action* (*Tails*).

Situation

Correct action

A Entry into a laboratory

B Using apparatus

C Setting up apparatus

D Using chemicals

E Using electricity

F When the lesson is finished

G When leaving bunsen burner unattend

1 make sure it is showing a yellow flame

2 Wash your hands thoroughly

3 Do not interfere with mains circuit or touch switches with wet hands

4 Never push or pull glass tubing into or out of a cork or a bung

5 Touch only when instructed to do so, and use only for their intended purpose

6 Do not enter any room without permission

7 Wear eye protection, check that the named substance is exactly what you want

Hazards — Safety

3) _Study_ the following sentences carefully and state if they are a _good_ idea or a _bad_ idea.

a) Place all waste material in a waste paper bin .... (G / B)

b) Never put solids, especially broken glass, in sinks .... (G / B)

c) Don't bother the teacher over minor cuts and burns .... (G / B)

d) Leave a blue flamed Bunsen burner unattended .... (G / B)

e) Be careful with clothing and long hair near a Bunsen flame .... (G / B)

f) When heating solids or liquids watch the mouth of the tube carefully .... (G / B)

g) It is safe to taste very small particles or droplets .... (G / B)

h) If you take a chemical into your mouth just swallow it .... (G / B)

i) If you get acid or alkali on your skin or clothing wash it off with hot water .... (G / B)

j) Chemicals spilled on the bench should be washed away immediately with cold water
and the area wiped clean .... (G / B)

k) Put waste paper in a bin .... (G / B)

Being Aware of how to be Safe

4) Study this picture of a science laboratory very carefully. List the _fifteen_ hazards in a table, like the one below.

Safety Hazards	
1	
2	
3	
4	
5	
6	
7	
8	
9	
10	

5) What do the following hazard signs indicate?

Top Tips: You know that safety is very important in the laboratory — you're not stupid. Use these questions as an opportunity to think about what you need to do to really be safe in your practical lessons. You might think you know it all _already_, but it's still well worth being _sure_. What it comes down to is _think_ first, follow the _rules_, think about _other peoples'_ _safety_ as well as your own, and don't be an _idiot_ if you can help it.

SECTION ONE — INTRODUCTION TO BASIC SKILLS

1

1

body

4

4

The Microscope

Much of the living world is too small for human eyes to see directly — the magnifying and resolving power of the eye is just not good enough. The microscope is an instrument used for viewing objects too small for us to see with the naked eye. The first simple microscope had only one lens, whereas those used today employ a series of lenses, and are called <u>Compound Microscopes</u>.

1) Look at the diagram of a Compound Microscope. <u>Copy</u> and <u>complete</u> the table below, listing the names of the microscope parts and their function.

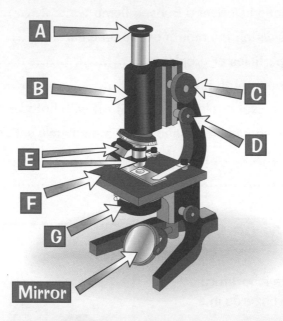

Mirror

Label	Name	Function
A		The lens closest to the eye. It magnifies by 10x
B	Body tube	Tube to support the series of lenses
C		For changing the distances between the lenses and the stage. It is used for rough low power focusing
D		For bringing object into sharper focus
E	Iris diaphragm	
F	Stage	
G	Low- and high-power objectives	

Using the Microscope

2) Using the word list below <u>copy and complete the passage</u> by putting the words in their correct places.

mirror	direct sunlight	dry	towards	eyepiece	wipe
	low power objective	away			

View the object through the _____ and adjust the _____ to obtain maximum brightness. Do not use _____ or this will damage your eyes. Keep the stage clean and _____, and always _____ the underside of the slide. Start first with the _____ _____ _____ and focus by moving the lens _____ or _____ from the slide.

SECTION ONE — INTRODUCTION TO BASIC SKILLS

The Microscope

The Field of View (F.O.V.)

3) When looking down the microscope a clear circle is seen. This is called the _Field of View_ (F.O.V.).

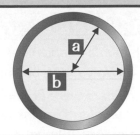

a) The diagram on the right shows the field of view with two lines marked. Which line, a or b, is the diameter of this field of view?

To find the actual size of something when viewing it through a microscope, we must first know the actual length the diameter of the F.O.V. corresponds to. We then compare the apparent size of the object seen through the microscope to the diameter of the F.O.V..

If the F.O.V. diameter is given in mm, and the number of animal lengths in a F.O.V. diameter is known, the actual size of the object, in mm, is given by:

$$\text{actual animal length (mm)} = \frac{\text{field of view diameter (mm)}}{\text{number of animal lengths}}$$

b) Work out the actual lengths of the animals from the field of view diagrams on the right, assuming a low power objective was used and the field of view diameter is 4 mm. Write your calculation out as shown below.

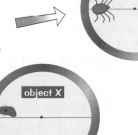

i) animal B:

Field of view diameter .... =____ mm

Number of animal lengths in a field of view diameter =____

Therefore animal B has an actual length of .... ____ mm

ii) animal C:

Field of view diameter .... =____ mm

Number of animal lengths in a field of view diameter =____

Therefore animal C has an actual length of .... ____ mm

c) The following specimen, object x, was looked at under a high power magnification, using a microscope which has a field of view diameter of 1mm.

Estimate the _length_ of object x.

4) The magnification of an object is the number of times the item has been enlarged from its actual size. This is calculated by multiplying the eyepiece magnification by the objective lens magnification. The eyepiece always magnifies things by 10 times, this is expressed as x10. The objective lens varies between a magnification of x5, x10, x20.

Complete the missing spaces in the table, assuming that the eyepiece always magnifies by a factor of 10.

Eyepiece	Objective	Total magnification
x10	x5	a) _ _ _ _
x10	b) _ _ _ _	100
c) _ _ _ _	x20	200
d) _ _ _ _	x10	e) _ _ _ _

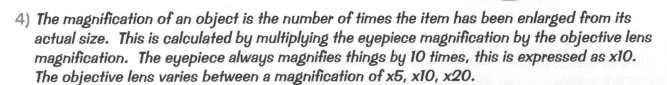

Top Tips:
You'll be using the microscope quite a lot, so you need to know _how to use it_ without _wasting time_ sitting around wondering what bit does what. You need to know how to work out the _real size_ of an animal and the _total magnification_.

Data Collection

Collecting Data

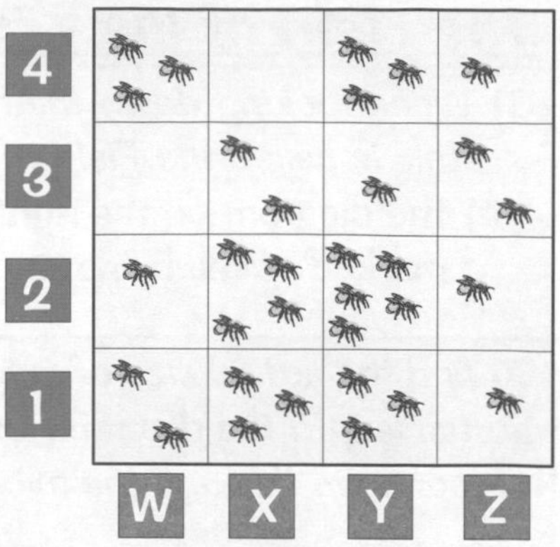

1) John's beehive has lots of bees in it (see diagram on the right).
   a) *How many* bees are there in the hive?

If there were hundreds or thousands of bees in John's beehive, it wouldn't be possible to count them all one by one. However, the total number can be *estimated* by dividing the hive into squares (as shown in the diagram), counting the number of bees in a few of the squares, and then multiplying up.

   b) *How many* bees are there in square W1? Multiply by the total number of squares to get an estimate of the total number of bees. How close is it to the true number?

   c) Repeat what you did for part (b) for each square Y2, Z4 and X1, individually. What do you *notice*? What are the *problems* associated with this method of estimating the total number of bees?

   d) The four squares W1, W2, X1 and X2 are combined to form a new, larger, square. This square covers *one quarter* of the total area of the beehive.
      i) *What* is the total number of bees in the new square?
      ii) *Multiply* the number of bees found in the new square by 4, to get a *new estimate* for the total number of bees in the hive. *How* does this answer compare to the actual total?

   e) *What* do your answers to (c) and (d) tell you about the benefit of increasing the sampling area when estimating the total number of bees present in the hive?

   f) In fieldwork, you may need to estimate the numbers of plants in a meadow, for example. The method is the same as shown above, but you use portable squares called *quadrats*, which are usually thrown backwards over your shoulder onto the ground. *Why* are quadrats thrown backwards over the shoulder rather than forwards?

Using Quadrats and Line Transects

2) Some students were studying a field near their school using 0.25m² quadrats. They were interested in three species of plant, A, B and C. The quadrat was thrown carefully over their shoulders ten times and the number of plants of each type was recorded each time. Their results are shown in the table on the right.

Sample number	Number of A	Number of B	Number of C
1	3	12	0
2	7	9	0
3	5	10	2
4	9	7	5
5	1	0	2
6	0	0	0
7	2	4	3
8	5	5	1
9	6	3	0
10	2	0	2

   a) What *area* (m²) was sampled in total?

   b) *How many plants* of species A were counted? Work out the species density for species A (the number of plants per m²). If the area of the whole field was 75m², estimate how many of species A there were in the whole field. Work out the species density and estimated total number for species B and C. *Show all your working out*.

   c) *How many times* was species A found *at least once* in a quadrat? Work out the *species frequency* for species A (the percentage of the total number of quadrats sampled in which species A was found at least once). Work out the species frequency for species B and C.

   d) The teacher noticed that the students had worked in a part of the field that was not shaded by trees. What might be the *effect* on their study of *avoiding the shade* of the trees in the field?

Data Collection

3) If plants occur in clumps, or the ground is sloping, a line transect is often used to sample the wildlife. A length of string is marked off at regular intervals and tied between two sticks along part of the habitat. Wherever a plant touches one of the marks, its distance along the line is recorded.

a) _Explain how_ recording the distances along the line transect to the markers touched by the plants, can yield information about the population density of a species of plant.

b) _What problems_ would be encountered using a quadrat to estimate the _number of each species_ of tree in a woodland? _What problems_ would be encountered using a line transect there?

Studying Populations of Organisms

4) Populations of animals are more difficult to estimate than populations of plants. One way to estimate a population of animals is the capture–recapture method. Some animals are caught, marked with non-toxic paint, and released. A day or so later some animals are again caught, and the number of marked animals is counted. The total population is estimated using the formula:

$$\text{Estimated population} = \frac{\text{Number caught first time} \times \text{Number caught second time}}{\text{Number of marked animals caught second time}}$$

a) _Explain_ why _animal_ populations are more difficult to estimate than _plant_ populations.

b) The manager of a fishing lake wanted to estimate the population of trout in the lake. Twenty fish were caught, and small rings were clipped onto their dorsal fins. The fish were released back into the lake. Two days later, 25 trout were caught. _Five_ of them had rings. _Work out_ the _estimated_ population of trout in the lake, using the formula above (_show your working_).

c) What would be the _estimated population_ of the trout if only _4_ fish had rings on recapture? What would be the _estimated population_ if _6_ fish had rings? Comment on the _reliability_ of this method.

d) Chris wanted to estimate the population of dark peppered moths in a wood. She caught 25 moths, put a bright spot of paint on their backs and released them. Two days later she caught 25 more moths, but none of them had a spot of paint. What has gone _wrong_ — why does Chris's experiment _imply_ that there is an infinite number of moths in the wood? _How_ could she _improve_ the experiment to get a _more accurate_ estimate of the population?

e) Dan wanted to estimate the population of tellins (small shellfish) in the sand on a beach. He dug up 100 tellins from a section of the beach, painted them with some nail varnish, and reburied them. A day later, he dug up 100 tellins from the same section of beach. All of them had a spot of nail varnish. What is the _estimated population_ of tellins on the beach? Do you think this result is _reliable_? If not, _explain_ what may have gone wrong with the experiment.

Studying Insects

5) There are several methods available to capture animals humanely for study. The pooter (right) is used for insects and spiders and other tiny creatures.

Look at the picture of the pooter. _How_ does it work?
There is often a mesh over the opening of the left-hand tube.
Why is this mesh needed?

Top Tips: All this looks a bit dense and complicated, but it really is _important_. You _have_ to use the correct methods to collect data, otherwise any results or conclusions you get might be wrong. _Sampling_, using _quadrats_, is used to estimate what is going on overall, because obviously you can't collect and look at every single specimen in a wood or a field.

Analysis and Interpretation of Data

Tables and their Many Uses

Tables are a very convenient way to show lots of data, and you may be asked in examinations to complete or draw up a table. Draw the lines with a pencil so that unwanted lines or errors can be erased. If you are recording measurements, the units should be put in the headings. If you are measuring a trend (e.g. the number of bubbles produced by pond weed when a light is shone on it from different distances) it is usual to make the first column the factor you are changing and the second column the factor you are measuring (see example above).

Distance of Light	Number of Bubbles in One Minute
10	23
15	11
20	6

1) Matthew did an experiment to look at the effect of insulation on the _rate of heat loss_ from beakers of hot water. He took the temperature every minute. His results are shown on the right. _Draw_ up a _suitable table_ for Matthew's results, and put his results into your table. _Explain_ why your table is a _better way_ of showing these results.

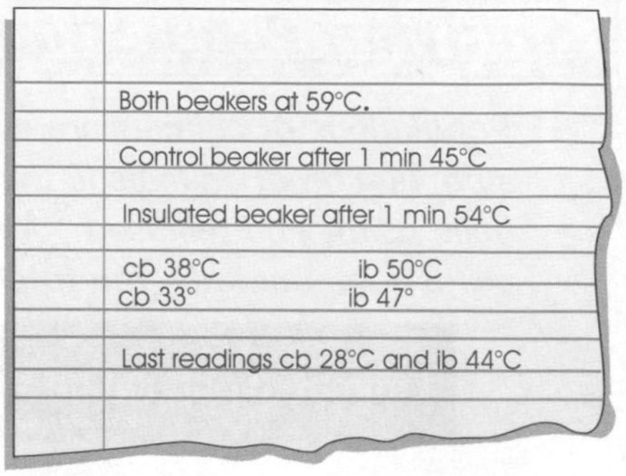

Both beakers at 59°C.
Control beaker after 1 min 45°C
Insulated beaker after 1 min 54°C
cb 38°C   ib 50°C
cb 33°   ib 47°
Last readings cb 28°C and ib 44°C

Pie Charts

Pie charts are very useful for showing data that are unrelated to another factor, e.g. percentage of different types of trees in a wood, percentage contribution of different sources of acid rain gases. You cannot use pie charts to show trends between two variables.

It seems obvious, but remember that there are $360°$ in a _full circle_. This means that each 1% is represented by $3.6°$ — this is tricky to plot accurately but you can buy protractors divided into percentages for drawing pie charts. In examinations, you will normally be given guide lines to help plot or interpret the pie chart (see diagrams below). These are normally ruled at $18°$ intervals.

2) _How many_ 18° segments are there in a circle? What _percentage_ of $360°$ does 18° represent?

3) Look at the unlabelled pie charts on the right. _What percentage_ of the full circle does the shaded segment in each case represent?

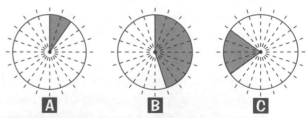
A   B   C

4) _Draw_ four pie charts having shaded segments of 5%, 25%, 60%, 85%, respectively. When drawing pie charts, the different segments should be labelled by writing the label outside the circle next to its segment. It often makes the chart clearer if you also write the value with the label, e.g. "power stations 34%". To make things clear, draw a line from the label to the small segments.

5) _The pie chart on the right shows the contributions of various countries to the world's greenhouse gas emissions. Work out the percentage of greenhouse gas emission for each country, including "others". Present your findings in a suitable table._

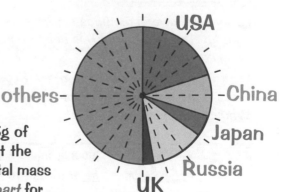

6) A can of baked beans contains 22.5g of protein, 11.25g of sugars, 18.75g of starch and 22.5g of fibre. Work out the _total mass_ of the contents. What _percentage_ of the total mass does _each nutrient_ constitute? Draw a _table_ and _pie chart_ for this information.

Analysis and Interpretation of Data

Bar Charts

A bar chart is a good way to present data showing a trend or pattern. It is useful for comparisons. In the Exam you may have to draw a bar chart or complete one given to you. Label the axes including units of measurement where appropriate — and draw the bar lines with a ruler. If you have to complete a chart, make sure you stick to the same style.

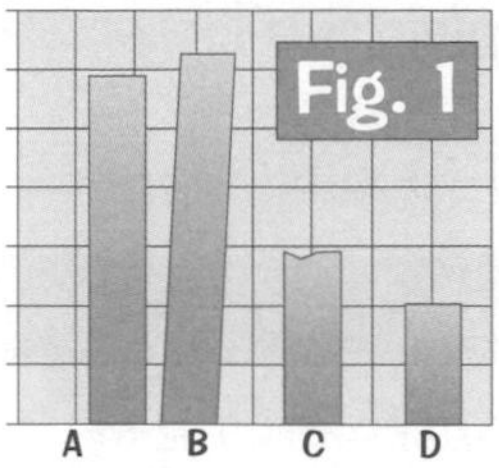

7) Study Fig. 1, the chart on the right. There are several things _wrong_ with this chart. _What_ are they? _Draw_ the bar chart correctly.

8) _The table below shows the lengths of some leaves._

Length of Leaf (mm)					
32	47	44	43	41	38
36	48	44	43	41	39
37	49	44	43	42	40
38	49	45	43	42	40

a) What are the _maximum_ and _minimum_ lengths?
b) _What_ is the _difference_ between the maximum and minimum length?

To plot a useful frequency histogram, you need to decide on a suitable _bin width_ _(e.g. 31-33, 35-37, etc. etc.) when tallying the data. If the bin width is_ _too small_ _then every leaf might get its_ _own bar_, _but if the bin width is_ _too big_, _then every leaf might contribute to a_ _single bar_!

c) Decide on a _suitable bin width_ for these data, and _explain_ why you chose it.

d) _Draw a table_ with the headings shown on the right, tally the lengths for each category found in part (c), and complete your table. Draw a _suitable bar chart_ to display your results.

bin width (mm)	no. of leaves

9) Construct a _suitable table_ to display the results shown in the bar chart on the right (Fig. 2). _Fill in_ your table with the data from the bar chart. On graph paper, draw _your own bar chart_ using these results. _What region_ has the highest Summer temperature?

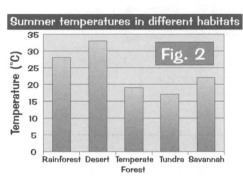

Line Graphs

A line graph shows trends and patterns where both the variables are continuous — like temperature and time. In the Exam, you may have to draw one or complete one given to you. Plot the points carefully and label the axes including units of measurement. Stick to the same style if you are adding data to a graph. If the points are not on a straight line, draw a smooth curve.

10) _What_ should you _remember_ to do when drawing each of the following?

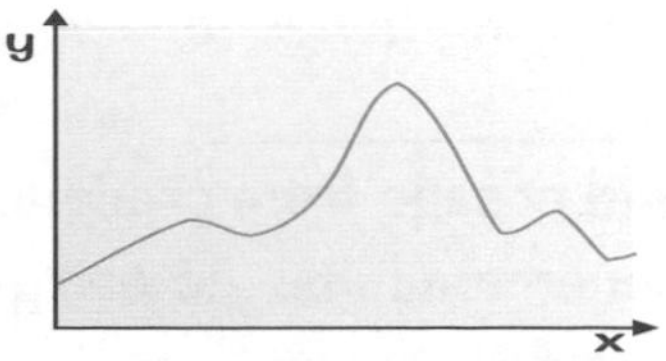

a) i) tables ii) pie charts iii) bar charts iv) line graphs

b) For _each_ of the following situations, explain whether a pie chart, bar chart or line graph is the _most appropriate_:
i) _heights_ of children in a class; ii) _amount_ of July rainfall in a field each year over a 10 year period; iii) _composition_ of gases in exhaled air; iv) _composition_ of gases in inhaled _and_ exhaled air; v) _change_ in temperature as a beaker of water cools down.

Top Tips:
More stuff you really need to know. The thing is, you've got to be able to record data so that _someone else_ could look at it and _understand it perfectly_. _Graphs_ and _tables_ are great ways to present data — you can summarise very large quantities of data which could be _almost unintelligible_ if it was just a _listing_ of results. Don't forget, you need to know where _each_ type of graph or chart is most appropriately used.

Life Processes

Life Process in Animals and Plants

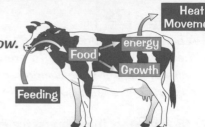

1) *The diagram opposite shows some of the life processes of a cow.*

 a) Name one life process that is <u>not shown</u> in the diagram.

 b) <u>Explain</u> this life process.

2) Next to each statement <u>fill in</u> the correct life process.

Observation	Life Processes Involved
a) One amoeba splits to form two individuals.	
b) When a gardener measured his bean plants, they had all increased in height by at least 5cm.	
c) After taking a plant out of a dark cupboard and shining light on it for at least 24 hours, there was starch in the leaves.	
d) On a kitchen window, cress plants bend towards the light.	

3) Draw lines to join the correct <u>life process</u> with the correct <u>description</u>.

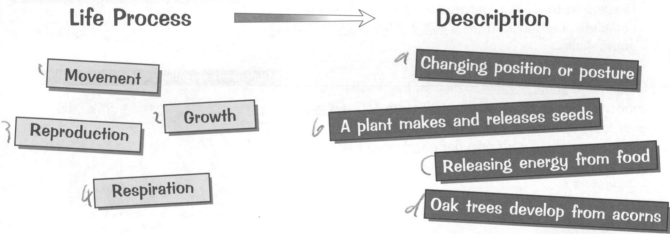

Life Process   Description

Movement

Growth

Reproduction

Respiration

a Changing position or posture

b A plant makes and releases seeds

c Releasing energy from food

d Oak trees develop from acorns

4) Use the words to <u>fill in</u> the spaces.

move	reproduce	sensitivity	nutrition
excreted	respiration	grow	

For living things to keep their species going from one generation to the next, they must
_____. Animals also need to _____ in order to find food, find a mate
and escape from predators. Living things produce new individuals that _____ to
become adults. To carry out the process of living, energy must be released from food. This is
called _____. We call the process of making or taking in food
_____. Inside our bodies we produce waste from chemical reactions. This is
_____ from the body. Living things must detect and respond to changes around
them. This process, known as _____, is very important for living things to survive.

Top Tips:
Let's face it, the Seven Life Processes are pretty easy. Mind you, it can be quite tricky <u>remembering</u> them all — but that's what <u>MRS NERG</u> is for. Make sure you learn <u>more</u> than just the names though — learn what they <u>actually mean</u>.

Cells

Plant and Animal Cells

1) These are two single-celled organisms that swim in water.

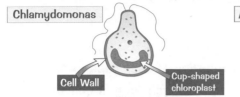

Chlamydomonas — Cell Wall, Cup-shaped chloroplast

Amoeba

a) Which one is more like a *plant cell*?

b) Give *two* reasons *why* it is more like a plant cell

2) Name *three structures* that both plant and animal cells have.

3) This is a diagram of a leaf cell.

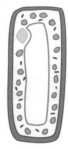

a) *Add* the following *labels* to the diagram:

cell membrane   cell wall   chloroplast

cytoplasm   nucleus   sap vacuole

b) What structures *enable* the leaf cells to make *sugar*?
c) What is the name of this *process*?
d) What is the name of the *green substance* found in leaves?
e) What is the *function* of the *cell wall*?

4) Complete the *blanks* using the words *below, (words may be used more than once)*.

cell membrane   cell wall   chloroplasts
cytoplasm   nucleus   sap   vacuole

Virtually all plant and animal cells have a _____, cytoplasm and a_____ _____. Plant cells are strengthened by a cellulose _____ _____. They also have a large, permanent _____ which contains _____. This is a liquid that contains stored substances and water. The water provides support for the cell. Chemical reactions take place in the _____ of the cell. A _____ controls the activities of the cell. It contains chromosomes which carry genes. The genes control characteristics. Plants make food in their leaf cells by photosynthesis. To do this, plants absorb light with chlorophyll which is found inside _____.

Animal and Human Cells

5) This is a diagram of a human sperm cell.

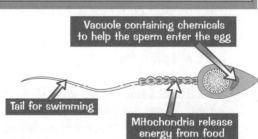

Vacuole containing chemicals to help the sperm enter the egg. Tail for swimming. Mitochondria release energy from food.

a) Name *two structures* found in the sperm cell that are not commonly found in animal cells.
b) Label two structures that are typical of *animal cells*.

6) Cells are grouped into tissues. Tissues are arranged together to form organs. Organs make up the systems.
a) Name the different *systems* in which you would find blood cells, brain cells, and the uterus.
b) What is *glandular tissue*?

Top Tips:
Cells are the basic building blocks of all life, so , surprise, surprise, they do tend to be come up in the Exams. They're a bit trickier than the life processes, but really not that bad. If you can learn the *four structures* that all cells have in common, and the *three* that *only* plant cells have, you'll be pretty much there — but do make sure you can recognise them all in a diagram. One last thing, you'll need to know this sequence: *cells → tissue → organ → organism* — and you've got to be able to define each term.

Specialised Cells

Cells and their Specific Functions

1) An ostrich egg could be considered to be the largest cell in the world. Which three main _features_ does it _share_ with a cell in the human body? What is the _function_ of the egg?

2) A, B and C in the diagram below are different types of cells.

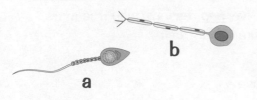 

a) _Name_ each type of cell.

b) What is the _function_ of each type of cell?

c) Give one feature of _each type_ of cell and say _how_ that feature _helps_ the cell to carry out its function.

3) Cells in animals and plants perform specific functions. An example is the jellyfish which has _stinging cells_ to protect itself from predators.

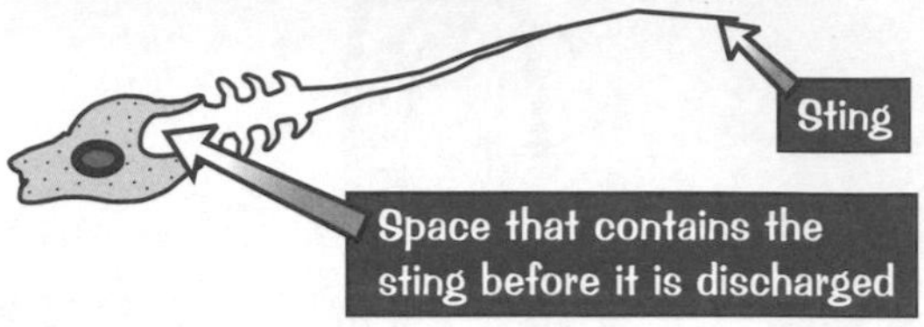

a) The diagram opposite shows a jellyfish cell. Label three _different structures_ that are present.

b) Name one other example of an animal cell, stating the _special job_ it does.

Sting

Space that contains the sting before it is discharged

4) On the surface of roots there are special cells called _root hair cells_.

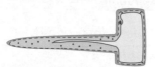

a) How are these cells _adapted_ to perform a specific function? Explain how the adaptation helps them carry out this function.

b) Name two _features_ shown in the diagram that tell us that this is a _plant cell_.

Blood Cells

5) The diagram below shows how _endothelial cells_ make up the structure of a blood capillary.

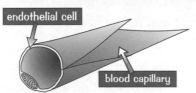

endothelial cell

blood capillary

Blood capillaries are fine blood vessels that allow substances to move across the endothelial cells. Substances like oxygen, sugar and other useful materials are passed out of the _capillaries_ and into surrounding cells.

a) From the diagram, explain how endothelial cells are _adapted_ to carry out their function.

b) Name one _substance_ that enters the capillaries from surrounding cells.

6) _White blood cells_ move inside blood vessels. What _function(s)_ are these cells adapted for and how do they carry them out?

White Blood Cell

7) _Red blood cells_ are _biconcave_ in shape — they curve inwards on both sides. They are also unusual because they have _no nucleus_. Oxygen _diffuses_ across the membranes of red blood cells, which then carry the oxygen to different parts of the body. These cells travel down capillaries which are only slightly wider than the cells.

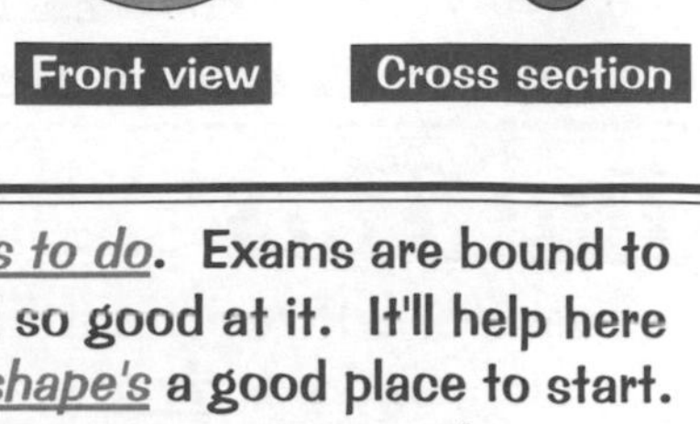

a) Red blood cells are _specialised_ cells. What does this mean?

b) Give one possible reason for: (i) the _shape_ of the cell.
(ii) the _lack_ of a nucleus.

Front view   Cross section

Top Tips:
Specialised cells are basically just cells with _jobs to do_. Exams are bound to ask you what that job is, or what makes the cell so good at it. It'll help here to look at all the bits of the cell, and see where they're different — the _shape's_ a good place to start. Of course if you've boned up on your cells, you'll sail through. Learn these seven in particular: _palisade_ leaf cell, _phloem_ cell, _xylem_ cell, _root hair_ cell, _muscle_ cell, _nerve_ cell, _sperm_ cell.

SECTION TWO — PLANTS

Diffusion and Osmosis

Sugar Solution Experiment

1) An experiment using the equipment on
   the right was set up.

   a) Explain why the distilled water in
      the beaker _became coloured_.

   b) Explain why the sugar solution _moved
      up_ the capillary tube.

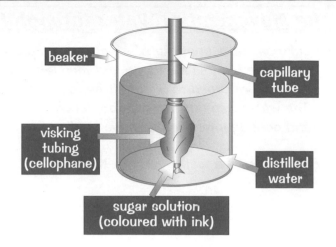

Water in Plants

2) Livadia is a Mediterranean village by the sea. In spring, there is flooding and the sea water

   rises and covers some of the nearby farmland owned by farmer Antonis. When this happens,

   Antonis has noticed that his crops begin to shrivel and die. _Explain why_ this happens.

Examples of Diffusion and Osmosis

3) For each of these sentences, indicate whether the process involved is _diffusion or osmosis_,
   by putting a "D" for _diffusion_ or an "O" for _osmosis_.

   a) Oxygen crosses the alveoli of the lungs and enters the blood.

   b) Water enters guard cells in the leaves from surrounding cells.

   c) Water moves from the moist stomatal space to the drier atmosphere.

   d) Water enters blood capillaries from surrounding body cells.

   e) Water in the soil crosses into the root hairs.

   f) Water is absorbed out of the kidney tubules and back into the blood stream.

   g) In the blood vessels in the lungs, oxygen enters red blood cells.

   h) Carbon dioxide enters stomata for photosynthesis.

A Practical Experiment

4) Kelly set up an experiment. She placed one prune in a beaker of distilled water and another
   in a very strong sugar solution (syrup).

   a) Kelly returned to her experiment 24 hours later. _Explain_ what you would expect to have
   happened to Prune A and Prune B.

14

Diffusion and Osmosis

The Movement of Water through Potato

5) Luke carved a boat out of a potato, and played with it in the kitchen sink. He placed salt inside the boat as his cargo and then left it sitting in the water for an hour while he had lunch. When he returned to his boat, he found that it had water inside. The water was not there before lunch and nobody interfered with his boat.

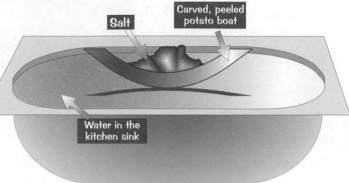

Salt

Carved, peeled potato boat

Water in the kitchen sink

Explain how the water got into the boat.

Understanding the Differences

6) Complete *the blanks* with these words.

| osmosis | diffusion | partially permeable | water molecules |
| high water | | low water | |

Osmosis is the movement of _____ _____ from a region of _____ _____ concentration to a region of _____ _____ concentration. In _____, water molecules move across a _____ _____ membrane. Osmosis is sometimes called a special case of _____ because water molecules move from a high to a low concentration of water molecules.

Diffusion and Osmosis in Plant Cells

7) This is a diagram of a *guard cell*:
Guard cells are found in leaves and form pores called stomata between them.

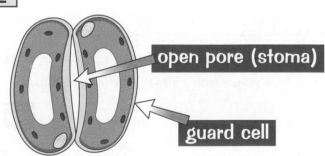

open pore (stoma)

guard cell

a) To bend and open the pore (stoma), guard cells must take up water from their surrounding cells.

i) What process is involved when water *enters* the guard cells?

ii) *Explain why* this process happens.

b) Gases can move through the stoma.

i) Name *two gases* that can enter leaves through the pores.

ii) What is the name of the *process* when molecules move in this way?

SECTION TWO — PLANTS

Diffusion and Osmosis

Sugar Solution and Potato Experiment

8) By pushing a cork-borer into a cut potato, two identical cylinders of potato were obtained. One cylinder was placed in a 20% sugar solution (a strong solution) and the other was placed in water.

a) _Explain_ what happens to the _length_ of each potato cylinder.

b) In another experiment, a range of different concentration solutions were made, from pure water to 20% sugar. It was noticed that the cylinder in one of the middle test tubes _did not change_ length. Explain this result.

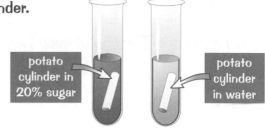

potato cylinder in 20% sugar

potato cylinder in water

Water Exchange in the Amoeba

9) An Amoeba is a single-celled organism found in pond water. Water from the pond continually enters the body of the amoeba. To prevent the amoeba bursting, it has vacuoles that collect water and release it to the outside.

a) By what _process_ does water enter the amoeba?

b) The pond water also contains the oxygen that the amoeba needs.
i) What is the _oxygen_ needed for?
ii) How does the amoeba get the _oxygen_ it needs?

c) i) Name one waste product that would be harmful to the amoeba if it could not get rid of it.
ii) By what process does this waste product get into the water?

d) Some amoeba live in the salty sea, but they do not have vacuoles. Why _don't_ these organisms _burst_?

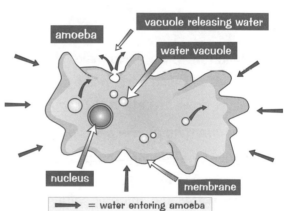

vacuole releasing water

amoeba

water vacuole

nucleus

membrane

= water entering amoeba

Movement of Water through Fruit

10) Joseph's mother showed him how she makes fruit salad. She cut fruit into a bowl and then sprinkled sugar all over the fruit. She placed the bowl in the fridge overnight. When she took out the bowl the following day, Joseph noticed that the fruit had liquid all around it. His mother then placed a few drops of food colouring in the middle of the bowl and again returned it to the fridge.

a) i) What is the _liquid_ in the bowl?
ii) Where did it come from?
iii) By what _process_ did the liquid appear in the bowl?

b) Later that day, Joseph noticed that the food colouring had spread through much of the liquid. What _process_ had occurred?

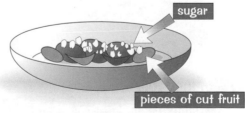

sugar

pieces of cut fruit

Top Tips: Things tend to _spread out_ — that's all diffusion is. And osmosis is just a special case of this — it's only called osmosis when you're talking about _water molecules_, and when it's across a _partially permeable membrane_ (make sure you can define this — you might be asked to). And they're both _random_ processes — so the organism doesn't have to expend any energy. If the _concentration gradient_ is in the wrong direction, it'll have to use _active transport_ instead — which _does_ need energy.

Plant Structure

The Construction of Plants

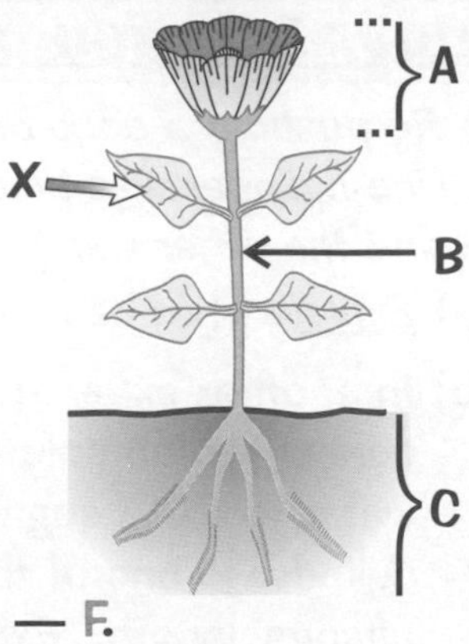

1) Look at the diagram on the right showing a typical plant.
   A plant is made up of <u>three main parts</u>.

   a) <u>Label</u> parts A, B and C.

   b) Give the name for the part of the plant marked with an X.

   c) Name the <u>function</u> of each part of the plant you have identified.

2) The flower structure contains the <u>reproductive organs</u> of the plant.

   a) From the diagram below match the given <u>names</u> to the structures A — F.

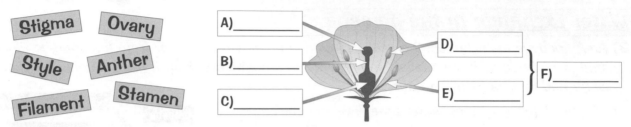

Stigma   Ovary   Style   Anther   Filament   Stamen

A)_____
B)_____
C)_____
D)_____
E)_____
F)_____

   b) Which of these parts make up the <u>female</u> reproductive organs?

   c) Which of these parts make up the <u>male</u> reproductive organs?

   d) What does structure D <u>produce</u>?

3) The stem holds the plant <u>upright</u>.

   a) <u>Give one reason</u> why plants need to be kept upright.

   b) *The stem contains many different kinds of cells.* What is the name given to the cells that carry <u>water</u> and <u>mineral salts</u>? Give one <u>feature</u> of these cells that <u>helps</u> them to carry water.

   c) What is the function of the <u>phloem cells</u>?

How Plants Adapt to their Habitat

4) <u>Leaves</u> are important organs in the plant. The diagrams below show three different types of leaves (these are drawn to <u>scale</u>).

Burdock

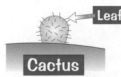

Leaf

Cactus

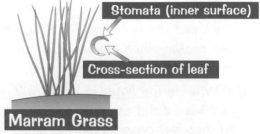

Stomata (inner surface)

Cross-section of leaf

Marram Grass

<u>Fill in</u> the table

Name of Plant	Possible type of habitat	Leaf Adaptation	Reason for adaptation

5) The roots are the parts of the plant that are found <u>below the ground</u>.

   a) Give <u>two functions</u> of roots.

   b) How have roots <u>adapted</u> to increase their surface area?

Plant Structure

6) Use the words to _fill in the spaces_ (the same word may be used _more_ than once).

flower	leaves	mineral salts	petals	roots	reproductive
seeds	stem	vascular bundles	water	xylem	

Plants can be divided into three parts; the _____, the stem and leaves, and the _____ under the ground. The roots hold the plant firmly in the ground. They also absorb _____ with dissolved _____ _____ from the soil. The water travels in the _____ cells to different parts of the plant. The xylem cells are found in the _____ _____ of the plant. The _____ has the function of holding the plant upright. This helps the leaves to capture more light. The _____ are organs responsible for making food. The flowers contain the _____ parts of the plant. These are enclosed in _____. After the flower is pollinated, _____ are released.

The Life Cycle

7) The diagram on the right shows the _life cycle_ of a plant. When a seed _germinates_ the root is the first part to grow. Then the leafy shoot appears above the ground. The seed normally contains food to _nourish_ the plant for the first few weeks of germination.

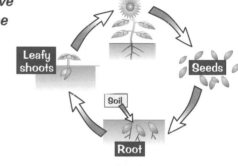

Leafy shoots — Seeds — Soil — Root

   a) Why does the root need to _grow first_?

   b) Why does the leafy shoot need to grow _above the ground_ within a few weeks?

   c) What will happen if the _seed_ was sown very _deep_ down in the soil?

8)

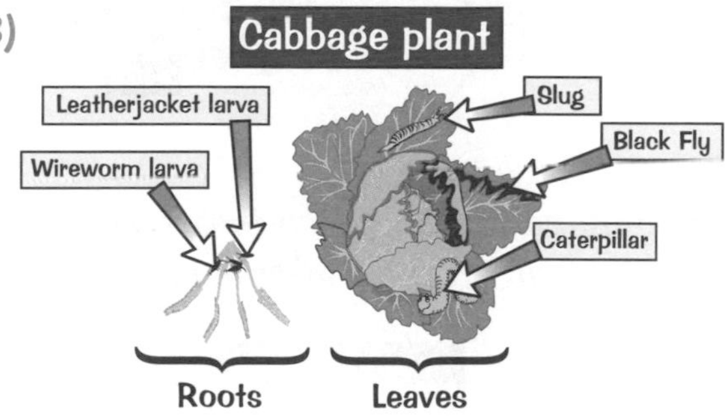

Cabbage plant

Leatherjacket larva — Slug — Black Fly — Wireworm larva — Caterpillar

Roots   Leaves

The diagram shows the parts of a cabbage plant that are eaten by _pest_ animals.

   a) More pest animals feed off the _leaves_ than the roots. Why do you think this is?

   b) Why does the plant _die_ when its roots are eaten?

   c) _Where_ do wireworm and leatherjacket larvae live?

9) The _Colorado beetle_ has spread from Colorado in America to much of Europe. It has been found in the UK since 1901. Both the beetles and their larvae feed on the leaves of _potato plants_. Originally, these beetles fed on buffalo burr (a plant native to the United States of America).

   a) _Explain_ why the beetle causes a _reduction_ in the number of potatoes, when it is only the leaves that are eaten.

Colorado Beetle

   b) What is the _function_ of potatoes?

   c) In what form is the _sugar_ made in the leaves _stored_ in the potato cells?

Top Tips: There's more to this than just knowing the _names_ of the various bits — you must know what they _do_ as well. It might help to think of the various _functions_ and which bits of the plant carry each of them out. Try these — _storage_, _reproduction_, _anchorage_, _growth_, _support_, and _transport_ of food and water.

Leaf Structure

The Construction of a Leaf

1) *The diagram opposite shows a section across a leaf.*

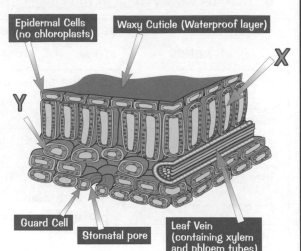

Epidermal Cells (no chloroplasts)

Waxy Cuticle (Waterproof layer)

X

Y

Guard Cell

Stomatal pore

Leaf Vein (containing xylem and phloem tubes)

  a) i) Give two _functions_ of a leaf vein.
    ii) Name the _cells_ carrying out each function.

  b) i) What name is given to the _pores_ in the leaf?
    ii) What controls the _size_ of the pores?
    iii) Why are there more pores on the
        underside of a leaf?

  c) i) Give the name for _cell_ X.
    ii) What is the _main function_ of this cell?
    iii) Give one way in which this cell is
        adapted for its function.

  d) i) Give the name for _cell_ Y.
    ii) These cells are rounded, creating large air spaces between them.
        Why is this _useful_ for the leaf?

  e) What is the function of the _waxy cuticle_?

Leaf Pores

2) *Most plants have more pores on the lower surface of their leaves.*

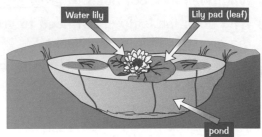

Water lily

Lily pad (leaf)

pond

  a) *Water lilies have more pores on their
     upper surface. Give a reason for this.*

  b) Name a _gas_ that the lily needs
     for photosynthesis.

  c) From the diagram, describe one _adaptation_
     of the water lily for photosynthesis.

Leaves and Greenfly

3) _Greenfly_ sit on leaves and pierce leaf cells with their mouthparts. They use their hollow
   mouthparts to extract food from the transport cells in the leaf. If a lot of greenfly are
   feeding on a plant, the plant can start to die.

Head of Greenfly

Hollow mouthparts

  a) What _part_ of the leaf do greenfly pierce?

  b) What type of _cells_ do they take food from?

  c) Give the name of the _food_ the greenflies are taking.

  d) In _which cells_ is this food made?

Table of Leaf Parts

4) _Match_ the _statement_ with the correct part of a leaf, for example A) — ii) or   B) — ii).

A) Contains chloroplasts

i) Palisade cell

B) Contains chlorophyll

ii) Chlorophyll

C) Green substance

iii) Chloroplast

D) Contains xylem & phloem cells

iv) Veins

Leaf Structure

The Function of the Waxy Cuticle

5) *Below is a cross-section of a marram grass leaf. Marram grass lives on sand dunes, where it is windy and there is a shortage of water.*

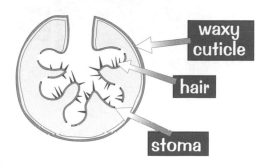

Marram grass leaf

waxy cuticle

hair

stoma

a) What does the *waxy cuticle* do?

b) i) How does the *position* of the stomata help this plant?

 ii) Why are there no stomata on the *outer* surface of the leaf?

c) Explain the function of the hairs on the inner surface of the leaf.

Banksia marginata is an Australian shrub. It is found in dry conditions and has sunken stomata.

d) Explain how having sunken stomata will affect gaseous exchange in the plant, and why this would be an advantage to the plant.

e) How would you expect the waxy cuticle of marram grass and *Banksia marginata* to be *different* from that of a plant that is found in *damp* places?

Variegated Leaves

6) *A variegated geranium has both green and white areas on its leaves.*

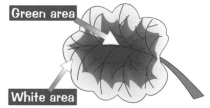

Variegated geranium leaf

Green area

White area

Cross-section of part of leaf

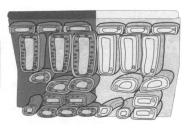

a) If the diagram were not shaded, how could you tell which cells were the green cells?

b) What *substance* makes these cells green?

7) Complete the blanks with these words:

carbon dioxide	chlorophyll	chloroplast	guard cells	mesophyll
palisade	stomata	veins	waxy cuticle	xylem

The leaf is the organ where food is made in a plant. Its _____ cells are packed closely together. These cells have many _____ which contain the green substance _____. This substance absorbs light. The spongy _____ is so called because it has many air spaces. The _____ _____ diffuses easily through these spaces to get inside the leaf cells. To make sugar, water is also needed. Water is transported to the leaf cells by _____ vessels. The transporting vessels are inside the _____ of the leaves. To prevent water loss, the surface of the leaf is covered by a _____ _____. To allow gases to move in and out of the leaf, there are many _____, mainly on the lower surface. The size of the stomatal pore is controlled by the _____ _____.

Top Tips: Knowing your *leaf structure* basically boils down to knowing the various *cell types*. There's only a few of them — but you've *really* got to know them. Make sure you can remember their *functions* and how they carry them out. Practise *drawing* them — then you'll be able to *recognise* them when they come up in the Exam.

SECTION TWO — PLANTS

Transpiration

Water Loss from the Pores in a Leaf

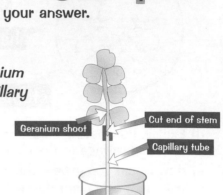

Pore

Layer of moisture

1) The diagram shows how water is lost from a pore in a leaf. 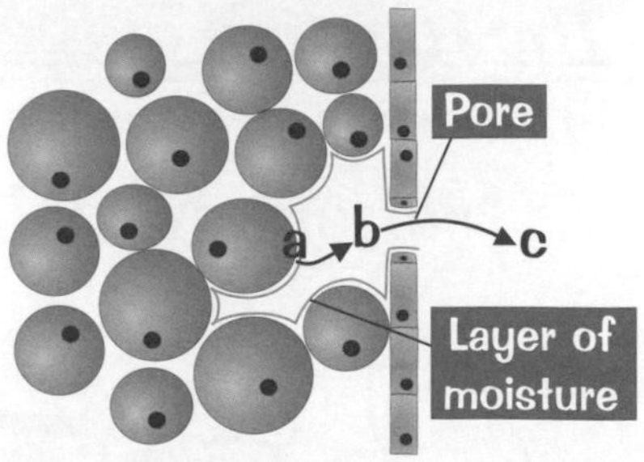
   a) Give the name of the *process* that occurs
         i) between *a* and *b*.   ii) between *b* and *c*.
   b) What *name* is given to the pore?
   c) What controls the *size* of the pore?
   d) Which *surface* of the leaf has more pores? Give a reason for your answer.

An Experiment Using a Potometer

2) The apparatus on the right is called a potometer. As the geranium stem draws water through the cut end of the stem up the capillary tube, the air bubble in the capillary tube moves up. 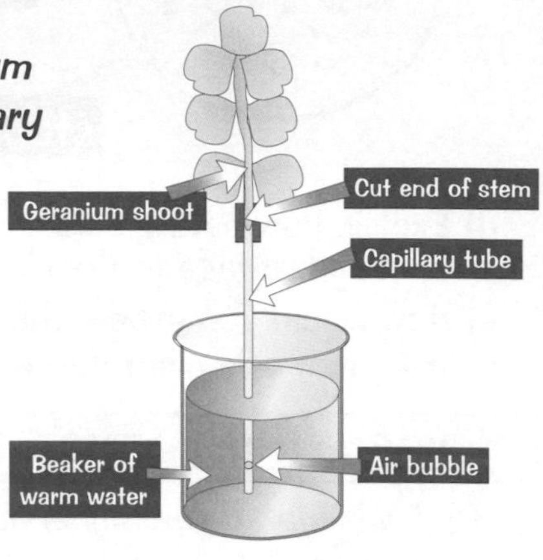
   a) Explain why the amount of water *lost* from the leaves is not the same as the amount of water *taken up* by the stem.
   b) By what process is water lost from the *surface* of the leaves?
   c) What type of *cells* does the water travel through to reach the leaves from the stem?
   d) What else is *transported* in these cells?

Geranium shoot

Cut end of stem

Capillary tube

Beaker of warm water

Air bubble

The Function of the Stomata

3) In most plants, the stomata are more open during the day and more closed during the night. In cacti (hot desert plants), the reverse is true.
   a) Give a possible reason for this.
   b) Explain exactly *how* the size of the stomata are controlled.

4) The table below gives the number of stomata found in five different species of plant. One of these plants is Oat, where the leaves are upright. This means that there is no clear lower and upper leaf surface.
   a) i) *Which letter* represents the oat plant?
      ii) Give one reason for your answer.
   b) Give two *functions* of stomata.
   c) i) Name an *atmospheric factor* that affects one of the functions.
      ii) Explain your answer.

Plant	Average number of stomata (per cm²)	
	Lower Surface	Upper Surface
A	2 300	2 500
B	16 100	5 100
C	46 100	0
D	26 300	6 000
E	1 900	5 900

5) The graph below shows what effect the size of the stomata has on the rate of transpiration. One curve shows what happens in still air and the other in moving air.

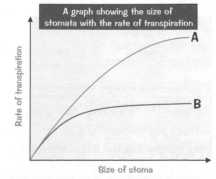

A graph showing the size of stomata with the rate of transpiration

Rate of transpiration

Size of stoma

A

B

   a) Which curve represents a plant that is surrounded by *still air*?
   b) How does the difference in air movement affect *the rate* of transpiration?
   c) Which curve resembles more closely what happens on a *hot day*? Explain your answer.

Transpiration

6) *A piece of blue cobalt chloride paper was stuck to the upper and lower surfaces of a leaf. Cobalt chloride turns pink as it becomes moist.*

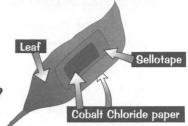

a) Which <u>surface</u> will turn the cobalt chloride pink first? Explain your answer.

b) What do we call the <u>process</u> by which water is lost from the leaf?

c) From where did the plant obtain the <u>water</u> that is lost from the leaf?

d) Give one condition that <u>slows down</u> water loss from leaves.

Clay Porous Pot Experiment

7) *This experiment shows water being lost from a porous clay pot.*

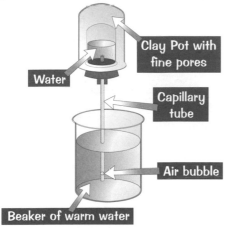

a) What is the name of the process by which the porous pot <u>loses water</u>?

b) State how each of these processes <u>affect</u> the amount of water lost from the <u>porous</u> pot:
   i) Increased humidity. ii) Greater light intensity.
   iii) Higher temperature. iv) Less wind.

c) What feature does the pot share with the leaf that allows it to lose water?

d) How does this feature differ between the pot and the leaf?

Growing a Plant Cutting

8) *Before a "cutting" grows roots, it is common to remove most of its leaves and cover it with a plastic bag.*
   a) Why are the leaves <u>removed</u>?
   b) Why is a plastic bag placed around a cutting?

9) <u>Complete</u> the blanks with these words.

| cuticle | evaporation | greater | guard | leaves | lower |
| stomata | temperature | thicker | transpiration | xylem | wilt |

Plants need to lose water by _____ in order to draw water through the plant. Streams of water travel through the _____ from the roots to the _____. The leaves have pores, called _____. It is through the pores that most water is lost. The size of the pores is controlled by _____ cells. Normally, a plant has more pores on the _____ surface of its leaves. Factors which affect _____ also affect the rate of water loss from the leaves. Factors include light, _____, air movements and the amount of moisture in the air. The drier the air is, the _____ is the loss of water from the leaves. If this loss were allowed to continue, the plant would _____. Leaves are covered by a layer of waxy _____ to prevent too much water being lost. Plants found in drier habitats generally have a _____ waxy layer.

Top Tips: Careful — transpiration <u>isn't</u> the same thing as evaporation: <u>transpiration</u> is the movement of a whole <u>water column</u> through a plant — it doesn't just happen at a surface. But since evaporation in the leaf draws the water up, they're affected by the <u>same things</u> — make sure you can list them. Don't forget the <u>potometer</u> experiment.

SECTION TWO — PLANTS

Transport Systems in Plants

Transport Systems in Plant Stems

1) On the right is a cross-section of a stem, showing the transport tissue of plants.

   a) i) Give the name for *tissue X*.
     ii) What is the *function* of this tissue?
   b) i) Give the name for *tissue Y*.
     ii) What is the *function* of this tissue?
   c) What is the name for *W*?

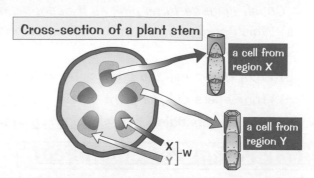

Cross-section of a plant stem

a cell from region X

a cell from region Y

2) High temperatures kill cells. When a steam jacket is placed around a stem of a tree, that part of the tree is heated to a high temperature. When this was done to a tree, it was noted that sugar no longer moved through the tree, but water did.

   a) What does this tell us about:

     i) the *phloem cells*?   ii) the *xylem cells*?

   b) In autumn it was found that the area above the steam jacket swelled. *Explain why* this happened.

   c) What *time of the year* would you expect the area below the steam jacket to swell? Explain your answer.

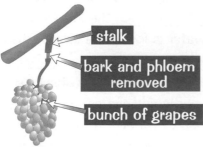

Steam Jacket

Steam

3) The diagram below right shows xylem and phloem cells.

   a) Explain why the ends of phloem cells are *perforated*.
   b) Explain why the xylem cells are *hollow*.
   c) Food is made in the leaves. What *parts* of the plant is it transported to?
   d) Give two uses of the *transported* food.
   e) What does the *transported* food consist of?

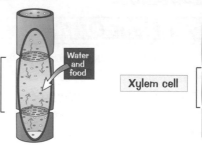

Water and food

Phloem cell

Xylem cell

Water and minerals

Practical Transport System Control

4) As grapes mature, they fill up with water and sugar. At the end of their growing season, grapes may lose some of their sugar back into the plant. The phloem vessels lie just under the bark of the stalk which holds the bunch of grapes. Grape growers sometimes remove the bark and phloem from the stalks holding bunches of grapes. This is done before the end of the growing season.

   a) Why is the *phloem* removed from the *stalk*?
   b) Why is the *xylem* kept intact?
   c) *Over-watering* can damage the grapes. *Explain* what might happen.

stalk

bark and phloem removed

bunch of grapes

5) The carbon dioxide in the flask shown contains radioactive carbon.

   a) What process uses the *carbon dioxide*?
   b) What *substance* does the radioactive carbon end up in *in the leaves*?
   c) What cells in the stem will *radioactive* material first appear in?
   d) Name the *substance* found in the stem cells that is radioactive.
   e) Name one other *structure* that the radioactive material will appear in.

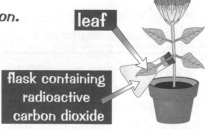

leaf

flask containing radioactive carbon dioxide

Transport Systems in Plants

The Movement of Water in a Plant

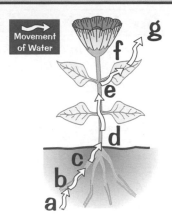

Movement of Water

6) *The diagram opposite shows the movement of water in a plant.*
   a) Name the *process* involved in moving the water from:
        i)   a to b   ii)   f to g
   b) What *carries* the water from d to f ?
   c) What is the name of the *spaces* in the leaf that allow water to escape to the *atmosphere*?
   d) What is the name given to the *column of water* that runs from the roots to the leaves?

The Function of Xylem Cells

7) *Xylem cells* transport water to different parts of a plant. These cells have a substance called *lignin* in their cell walls. *Lignin* makes structures waterproof and strong. The insides of xylem cells break down and the cells become empty tubes.
   a) How does *lignin* help xylem cells to carry out their function of transporting water?
   b) Give one feature of the *xylem cells* that enables water to move easily from one cell to the next?
   c) What do the xylem cells carry *besides water*?

8) *The word xylem comes from the Greek word for wood. Wesley placed one end of a wooden pole he found in his shed in coloured water. He noticed that the colour travelled up the wood.*
   a) What does this tell us about the *movement* of water in xylem cells?
   b) i) What is the name of the *other type* of transporting tissue?
        ii) What does this *tissue* transport?

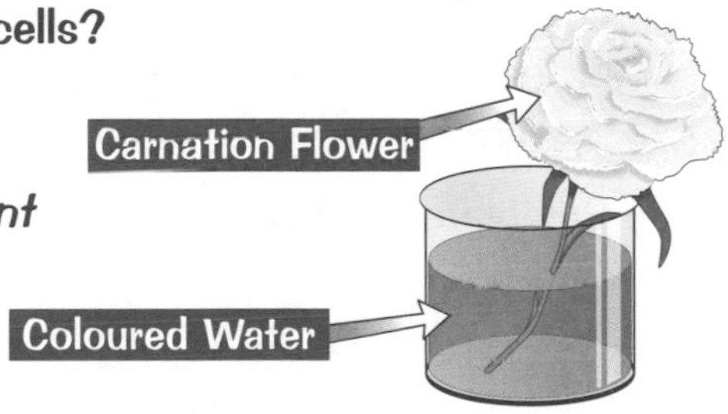

Carnation Flower

Xylem cells are found throughout the plant. All parts of the plant need water. This includes the petals of the flower.
   c) What do you think will happen if you cut off a white carnation flower and place the stalk end in red water?

Coloured Water

Aphids and Plants

9) *Aphids* use their mouthparts to pierce stems in order to get food.
   a) What *food substance* would you expect the aphid to be feeding off?
   b) What cells do the mouthparts pierce to extract the liquid?

Aphid

Plant stem

10) *Complete* the blanks with the words provided:

| cytoplasm, | living, | minerals, | photosynthesis, | respiration, | starch, |
| stem, | stream, | sugar, | transpiration, | vascular, | xylem. |

Plants have transport systems. The _____ tissue transports water from the roots to the _____ and leaves. The column of water that runs from the roots to the leaves is called the transpiration _____. Water loss from the leaves is called _____ and causes water to be pulled up through the plant. The water contains _____ from the soil. Phloem tissue carries dissolved food, such as _____ from the leaves, where it is made by _____, to the rest of the plant. The food is used for _____, making materials for cells and to produce _____ which is held in storage organs. The xylem and phloem cells are found in the _____ bundles of the plant. Xylem cells are dead and have no _____. Phloem cells on the other hand are _____.

Top Tips: *Phloem* — hmm, sounds a bit like 'flow-'em' — so it must be transporting stuff *downhill*. And whether it's going up or down the plant should tell you *what's* being transported. Make sure you know which is which in a diagram — the *phloem* cells (*alive*) are nearer the *surface* of the stem (closer to the *oxygen* they need) than the *dead xylem* cells.

Photosynthesis

The Function of Leaves

1) The diagram shows what the leaves need to make food.

   a) *Complete* the labels on the diagram.

   b) Name the *process* involved in making food.

   c) What is the name of the *food produced*?

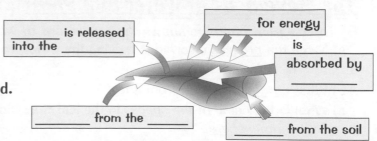

_____ is released into the _____

_____ for energy

_____ is absorbed by _____

_____ from the _____

_____ from the soil

Variegated Leaves

2) A variegated plant (its leaves have two colours) was placed in a dark cupboard for 48 hours to use up all of its starch. One of its leaves was then covered with a strip of black card across the middle. The plant was placed in the light for 24 hours. The leaf was then tested for starch.

   a) Shade in the areas on the unlabelled leaf to show where the *starch* was found.

   b) i) What *indicator substance* is used to test a leaf for starch?

   ii) What *colour* does the indicator turn when starch is present?

   c) Why was it *necessary* to get rid of the starch from the leaves?

   d) *Tick* or *write out* the correct conclusion(s) that can be drawn from this experiment.

   ... carbon dioxide is needed for photosynthesis   ... chlorophyll is needed for photosynthesis

   ... light is needed for photosynthesis   ... water is needed for photosynthesis

Light

Green part of leaf

White part of leaf

Black card

3) Complete the table.

	Photosynthesis	Respiration
Raw materials used		
End products		
Purpose of process		

4) *The graph shows* the exchange of carbon dioxide between a plant and its surrounding environment.

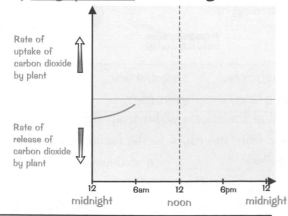

Rate of uptake of carbon dioxide by plant

Rate of release of carbon dioxide by plant

12 midnight   6am   12 noon   6pm   12 midnight

a) Why is the rate of release of *carbon dioxide* into the atmosphere declining between midnight and 6am?

b) Complete the curve to show *what happens* between 6am and 6pm.

c) Place an **X** on the graph to show when the rate of carbon dioxide *released* is exactly balanced by the rate of carbon dioxide *absorbed*.

Light and Photosynthesis

5) The graph shows the rate of photosynthesis and the wavelength (colour) of light used.

   a) Which *wavelengths* (colours) are most important for photosynthesis?

   b) What substance *absorbs* these wavelengths of light in plants?

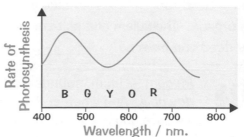

Rate of Photosynthesis

B G Y O R

400   500   600   700   800
Wavelength / nm.

Colour of Light
O = Orange
R = Red
B = Blue
G = Green
Y = Yellow

Photosynthesis

6) *Adam set up a bottle garden. Inside the bottle he grew some plants and placed a butterfly he caught in his garden. He knew the butterfly fed on sugar, so he placed a dish of sugary water inside the bottle. Just before going on a two week holiday to Corfu, Adam caught another butterfly. He placed this butterfly in another bottle, but he did not have time to add the plants. The diagrams show what he saw when he returned from holiday.*

a) Why did the butterfly in the second bottle *die*?

b) Besides its droppings, what does the first butterfly *produce* that will help the plants to grow?

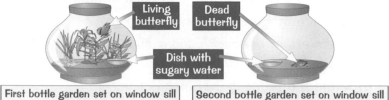

Living butterfly | Dead butterfly | Dish with sugary water

First bottle garden set on window sill | Second bottle garden set on window sill

7) *A plant was left in a dark cupboard for 48 hours to make sure it had no starch in its leaves. The plant was then set up in a bell jar as shown in the diagram. The apparatus was then left for 24 hours and the leaves tested with iodine. Place ticks in the correct boxes.*

Leaf	Turns blue/black	Has starch
A		
B		
C		
D		

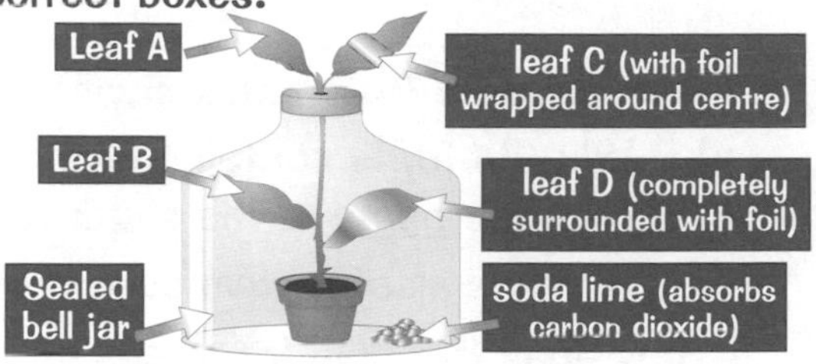

Leaf A | leaf C (with foil wrapped around centre)
Leaf B | leaf D (completely surrounded with foil)
Sealed bell jar | soda lime (absorbs carbon dioxide)

8) *Complete* the following equation for photosynthesis:
   a) with words   b) with chemical symbols

_____ energy

_____ _____ + _____   ➞   _____ + _____

absorbed by _____

The Rate of Photosynthesis

9) *The graph shows the effect of different conditions on the rate of photosynthesis.*

a) Name a factor that *limits* the rate of photosynthesis at *position X*.

b) Draw a curve on the graph to show what would happen if the amount of carbon dioxide was *increased* to a much higher level (at 30°C).

c) What is a *limiting* factor?

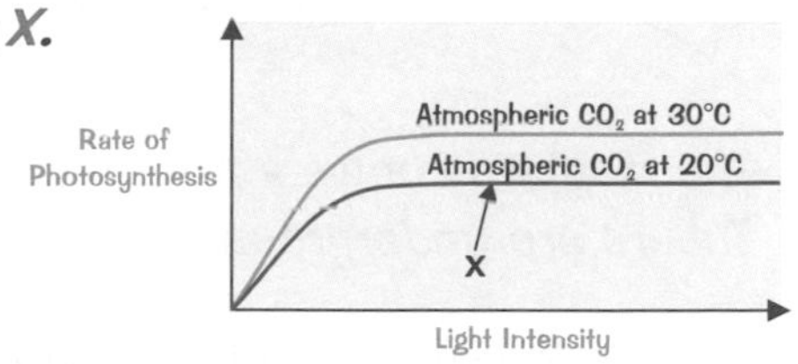

Rate of Photosynthesis | Atmospheric CO_2 at 30°C | Atmospheric CO_2 at 20°C | X | Light Intensity

10) *Four test tubes were set up as shown in the diagram, with hydrogencarbonate added to the tubes as an indicator. The table records the colour of the hydrogencarbonate in each tube after one hour.*

RESULTS

Tube	Colour of hydrogencarbonate indicator after one hour
a	Yellow
b	Purple
c	Orange
d	Orange

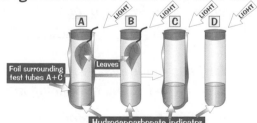

A | B | C | D | LIGHT
Foil surrounding test tubes A+C | Leaves
Hydrogencarbonate indicator

a) Which tubes act as *controls*?

b) i) What *substance* do you think made the indicator turn *yellow* in test tube a?
   ii) What *process* produces this substance?

c) i) Why do you think the indicator turned *purple* in test tube b?
   ii) What *process* is occurring in test tube b that does not occur in test tube a?

Top Tips:
Photosynthesis is a pretty basic life process, so you'll definitely need to know it for the Exam — *equations* and all. Don't forget the *differences* between photosynthesis and respiration, as this often crops up. Other than that, you need to know the relevant *structures* in the leaf — and remember what *photosynthesis* has to do with *transpiration*.

Food and Plants

Glucose and Sugar in Plants

1) The diagram on the right shows some of the uses of glucose by plants.
   a) i) Name five structures that _store_ food in plants.
      ii) Give the name of the food each structure stores.
   b) Why are storage substances _insoluble_?
   c) _Fruits are swollen with sugar and water._ How does this _help_ the plant?
   d) Name the _process_ that makes glucose.
   e) _Energy can be released from glucose._ What is the name of _this_ process?
   f) Name _two_ substances that are made from glucose.

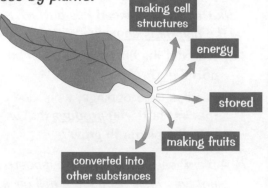

2) A strawberry fruit tastes sweet because of the sugar inside it.
   a) i) Why do fruits contain _sugar_?
      ii) Give the _name_ of the sugar found in fruits.
   b) _The seeds also contain substances made of sugar._ How does this help the _seeds_?

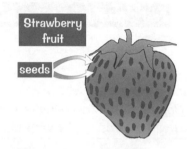

Starch and Glucose in Plants

3) This is a long chain molecule of starch.

X

starch molecule

   a) _Name_ X.
   b) What substances are produced when X is _combined_ with nitrates?

4) The diagram shows a potato plant with swollen tubers. Tubers are underground stems that swell with starch.

   a) Why is starch used as a _storage_ substance?
   b) Why does the potato plant make _tubers_?
   c) _Starch is made from glucose._ Where does the glucose used by the tuber _originate_?

potato tubers

5) A student has made two models of a cell. One has starch in it, the other contains glucose. Both are placed in test tubes containing pure water.

   a) Which model becomes _swollen_?
   b) What is the _name_ of the process that causes the 'cell' to _swell_?
   c) Explain _why_ the 'cell' swells.
   d) Give one advantage of cells _storing_ starch.
   e) Name one other storage _substance_.
   f) Name an _organ_ whose cells could be represented by model 'b'.

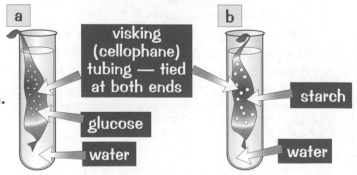

Food and Plants

Plant Storage Organs

6) Match up each *plant* with the correct storage *organ*.

Carrot, Plum, Pea, Cabbage, Potato

root, fruit, tuber (underground stem), seed, leaves

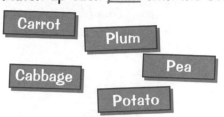

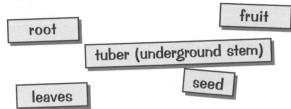

Oil from Plants

7)

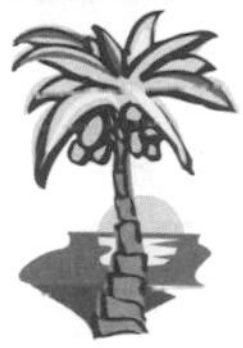

Oil-palm trees have fruits that are rich in oil. Oils and fats are called lipids. The diagram on the right shows how oil is produced and some of its uses.

chemical process in the leaves
substance X
oil in fruits
used to make
cooking oil
margarine
detergents and soap

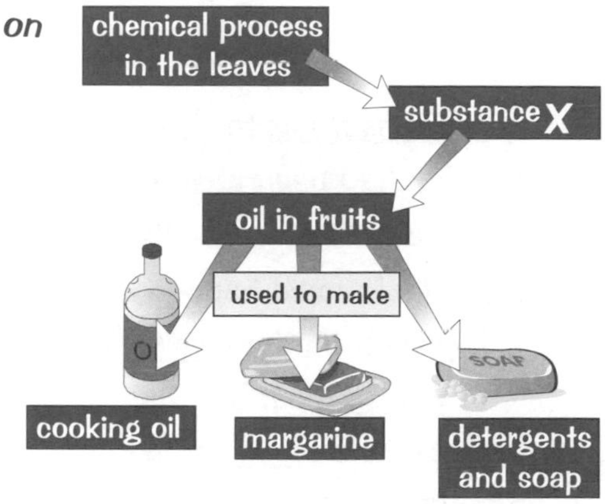

a) What is the name of the *process* that takes place in the leaves?

b) What is *substance* X?

c) Name another substance that can be *made* from X.

d) Name three possible *storage organs* visible in the picture of the oil-palm tree above.

8) *The flow diagram below shows how proteins are made.* *Fill in the gaps* to complete the diagram.

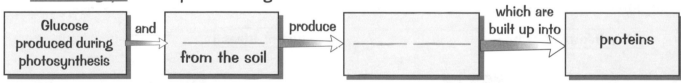

Glucose produced during photosynthesis → and → __________ from the soil → produce → __________ __________ → which are built up into → proteins

9) *Complete* the spaces with these words.

active ***cellulose*** ***glucose*** ***insoluble*** ***larger*** ***lipids*** ***proteins*** ***respiration*** ***sucrose*** ***starch*** ***stems***

When photosynthesis takes place, __________ is produced. Glucose can be converted into the storage substance __________. This substance is __________, therefore stopping cells from swelling with water. Starch is stored in the roots, __________ and leaves. Glucose is changed into __________ before being stored in fruits. In seeds, though, glucose is often made into __________. Amino acids can also be made from this sugar. The amino acids can be joined together to form __________. Glucose can be turned into __________, found in cell walls. This strengthens the walls and helps to give plants support. The release of energy from glucose is called __________. Energy is used to build smaller molecules into __________ molecules. It is also needed for __________ transport. This enables minerals to move into the roots of a plant against a concentration gradient.

Top Tips: I reckon there's nothing too complicated here. It's just a case of learning all the ways plants *use* the *glucose* formed in photosynthesis. Think of all the different *substances* it gets converted into, *how* they are used, and *where* in the plant this happens. These are the important ones — *starch*, *sucrose*, *lipids*, *cellulose* and *amino acids*.

Hormones in Plants

Growing Plant Shoots

1) *A number of freshly cut shoot tips were placed on a block of agar jelly. After a while the shoot tips were discarded and the jelly was then cut into smaller blocks of equal size. One block was placed on each of three shoots that had had their tips removed. Two of the blocks were placed off-centre, as shown in the diagram below. The blocks were labelled X, Y and Z.*

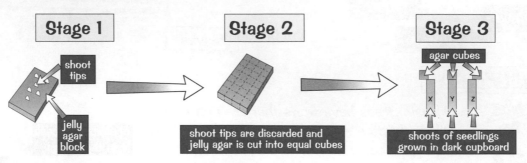

Stage 1 — shoot tips / jelly agar block

Stage 2 — shoot tips are discarded and jelly agar is cut into equal cubes

Stage 3 — agar cubes / X Y Z / shoots of seedlings grown in dark cupboard

a) *What happens* to the shoot labelled: i) X, ii) Y, iii) Z ?

b) What had been absorbed by the agar in *Stage 1* that affected the shoots in *Stage 3*?

c) Explain exactly how this had the effects you described in part a).

d) i) What would happen to X if more cut shoots had been placed on the *original* agar jelly block?

   ii) *Explain* your answer.

   iii) Draw a *curve* on the graph showing the trend you would expect.

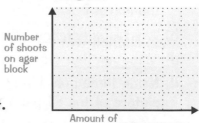

Number of shoots on agar block

Amount of _____

The Direction of Plant Growth

2) *Mrs Smith, the science teacher, showed the class a demonstration.* Which of the students' ideas are *correct*?

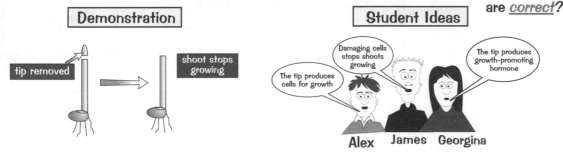

Demonstration — tip removed / shoot stops growing

Student Ideas —
The tip produces cells for growth (Alex)
Damaging cells stops shoots growing (James)
The tip produces growth-promoting hormone (Georgina)

3) *These are shoots with razor blades pushed into them.*

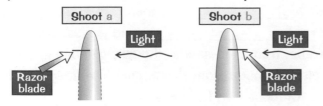

Shoot a — Light / Razor blade

Shoot b — Light / Razor blade

a) Explain in which direction *shoot a* would grow?

b) Explain in which direction *shoot b* would grow?

4) *A young broad bean seedling was placed in the ground sideways.*

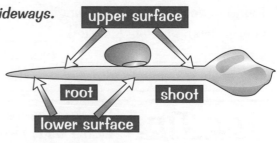

upper surface / root / shoot / lower surface

a) i) In which *direction* does the *root* grow?
   ii) *What causes* the root to grow in this direction?
   iii) What *stimuli* affect the direction of root growth?

b) i) In which direction does the *shoot* grow?
   ii) *What causes* the shoot to grow in this direction?
   iii) What *stimuli* affect the direction of shoot growth?

c) What name do we give to the main *chemical* controlling the growth of the shoots and roots?

d) What effect does this chemical have on the *cells* of the shoot?

Hormones in Plants

5) Complete the _blanks_ with these words (*words may be used more than once*).

auxin	bushier	fruits	geotropic	gravity	growth
hormones	moisture	phototropic	roots	seedless	shoots

Plant _____ grow towards the stimulus of light and against the force of _____. The plant _____ grow towards the stimulus of gravity and _____. We say that shoots are positively _____ and that roots are positively _____. Plants produce chemical _____ to coordinate and control growth. The shoot tip produces the hormone _____. This hormone causes shoot cells to elongate. When unidirectional light shines on one side of the plant, the auxin accumulates on the other side. This promotes uneven _____ in shoots, bending the shoot towards the light. Rooting powders contain the same hormones. These will promote _____ to grow on shoot cuttings. Unpollinated flowers can be treated with hormones to produce _____ fruits, such as grapes. The ripening of _____ can also be regulated with hormones. Broad-leaved selective weedkillers, such as 2-4 D, also contain hormones. These work by disrupting the normal _____ of broad-leaved plants. The hormones produced in the shoot tip inhibit side shoot growth. Removing the tips of shoots encourages the growth of _____ plants.

6) Complete the boxes in the table.

Chemical Involved	How is it used?	What effect does it have?
Rooting hormone		
	Sprayed over broad-leaved weed plants	
		Produces fruit without any pips

Controlling Plant Growth

7) *Tony decided that he was going to grow the straightest corn shoots possible.*

a) What could he do to corn seedlings to make them grow _straight_?

b) *Two weeks after growing the seedlings, Tony noticed that the shoots were growing to the left.* Give a possible reason for this, and explain how Tony could _make_ the seedlings grow straight again.

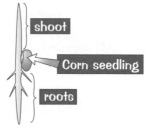

8) *The diagrams show four boxes. Each of the boxes is placed in the same uniform environment, and has one cress plant placed inside it.*

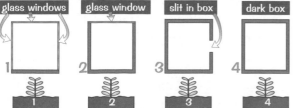

Cress plants before being placed in their respective boxes

a) _Redraw_ the boxes, showing inside each the _appearance_ of the cress plant after a few days.

b) For each box _explain_ the pattern of growth you have drawn.

9) Complete these sentences by choosing the correct word or words from inside the brackets:

a) If growth hormones are applied to (_pollinated_/_unpollinated_) flowers, seedless fruits are produced.

b) Selective weedkillers act on plants by (_disrupting_/_stopping_) the growth of the plant.

c) Cutting the tips of plants makes them grow (_bushier_/_taller_).

d) Fruits can be (_made to ripen_/_made to stay unripe_) when they are sprayed with hormones.

Top Tips: It should be pretty obvious what way shoots and roots grow in response to _light_ and _gravity_ — but you must be able to _name_ these responses and know how _hormone levels_ cause them — that's what the Exams will ask. And you'd do well to know how growth hormones are used _commercially_ — examiners always like to test you on the _applications_ of science.

Nutrition

Consuming Food

1) If somebody tells you they are on a diet, it usually means they are trying to lose weight. However, to a scientist we are all on a diet even if we are tucking into lard butties and loads of chocolate! What does _diet_ mean to a scientist?

2) Name _four_ things that animals need food for. Explain why plants _don't_ need to eat food.

3) Explain what the words herbivore, carnivore and omnivore mean. Give _examples_.

4) _Match_ the nutrient to its correct use:

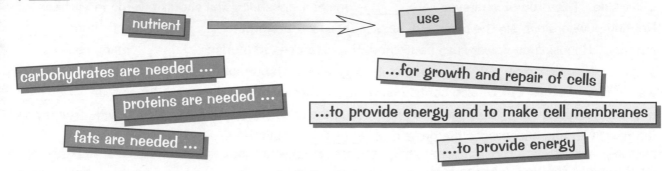

5) It is important that you remember which foods are good sources of the three main nutrients.
   a) Write down three examples of foods that are good sources of _carbohydrates_. Do you notice anything about foods that are _rich in carbohydrates_?
   b) Write down three examples of foods that are a good source of _protein_. Do you notice anything about foods that are _rich in protein_?
   c) Write down three examples of foods that are a good source of _fat_. Do you notice anything about foods that are _rich in fat_?

A Balanced Diet

6) Vitamins take part in chemical reactions in the body. They are only needed in small amounts, but without them we would not be healthy. Write down two examples of foods that are good sources of _vitamin C_, and two examples of foods that are good sources of _vitamin D_.

7) Minerals are very important in maintaining a healthy body. One of them, fluoride, is found in milk and in some areas, tap water. It is needed to maintain hard tooth enamel (it is also added to most toothpaste, but don't eat it — too much fluoride is poisonous and can damage teeth!)

   a) Which foods are good sources of the minerals _iron_, _calcium_ and _sodium_?
   b) _Why_ do our bodies need these minerals?

8) We need 20-30g of dietary fibre (roughage) a day. A can of baked beans contains over 20g of dietary fibre. _Write down_ two other sources of dietary fibre. Why do we need _fibre_ in our diet?

9) We each need about 3 litres of water a day. It is often recommended that we drink plenty of water, and food also contains water. Why do our bodies need plenty of water?

10) _Make a table_ with the headings shown on the right.
   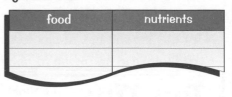
   In the _food_ column, _write_ the following foods:
      cereals, vegetables, fruit, meat, fish, dairy products.
   Then _choose_ nutrients from the following list which are found in each food, and write them in the _nutrient_ column:
      vitamin C, protein, iron, dietary fibre, carbohydrate, fat, vitamin D, calcium.

11) Explain what a _balanced diet_ means.

Nutrition

Energy Content of Food

12) *A calorimeter is needed to measure the energy content of food accurately, but an approximate measure can be made using the apparatus shown in the diagram below.*
   A piece of food such as a crisp or other snack food is stuck on a pin, set on fire, and used to heat a measured amount of water. The starting and finishing temperatures of the water are recorded. The greater the rise in temperature, the more energy released. You can then compare the energy content of different foods.

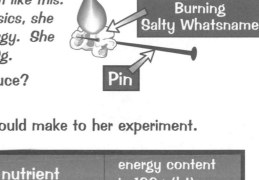

   a) What factors would you keep constant to make such an experiment a *fair* test?

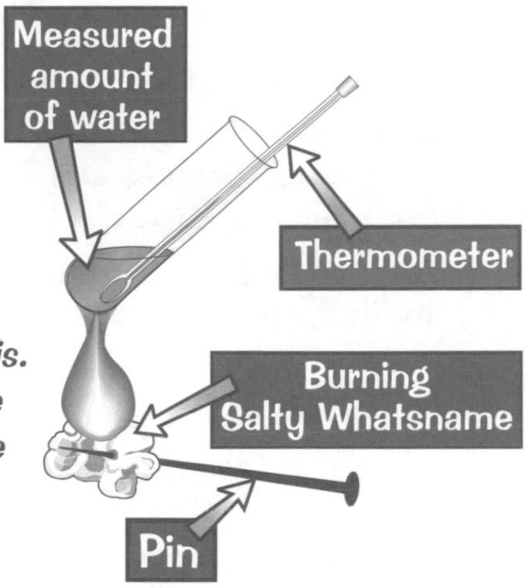

   A keen student burned a Salty Whatsname in an experiment like this. After the sort of calculations you do in Chemistry and Physics, she found that 1g of the delicious snack produced 15 kJ of energy. She read on the packet that it should produce 2500 kJ per 100g.

   b) How much *energy* should 1g of Salty Whatsname produce?
   c) Explain why the student got a *different value*.
   d) Suggest some *simple improvements* that the student could make to her experiment.

Calorie Content

13) Study the information in the table on the right.

   a) If you were trying to lose weight, *which nutrient* would you try to reduce in your diet?
   b) *Fats are found in dairy products.*
      Explain the *disadvantages* of reducing dairy product intake in the diet.
   c) *How much* energy would you get from 1g of fat? *Show your working out*.
   d) *Teenage girls need about 9250 kJ a day, and teenage boys need about 12210 kJ a day.*
      Work out the *mass of fat* needed to provide these amounts of energy.
   e) *It is generally recommended that fats should provide no more than 30% of your energy intake.*
      i) What mass of fat would that be in each of the boys and girls diets?
      ii) What mass of *carbohydrate* or *protein* would need to be eaten to get the other 70%?
   f) *Four types of nutrient provide no energy to the body at all. What are they?*

nutrient	energy content in 100g (kJ)
carbohydrate	1700
protein	1700
fat	3700

14)

PATA'S ITALIAN PASTA HELICES	
Nutritional information	
Typical values	Per 100g
Carbohydrate	27.4g
Protein	4.6g
Fat	0.4g
Fibre	0.9g

MURINE BRAND GRATED CHEESE	
Nutritional information	
Typical values	Per 100g
Carbohydrate	0.6g
Protein	25.0g
Fat	34.4g
Fibre	less than 0.1g

Look at the two *food labels* above. Use your knowledge of nutrition to *evaluate* each of the two foods. You should mention the *likely benefits* of eating each food and point out any *drawbacks*.

Top Tips:
You've had plenty of *practical* experience of food in your life already. Now you need to know the *seven* main groups of nutrients, *where* they are found, and what we *need* them for. Don't forget — *water* is more important to survival than you might think. Remember how you measure the energy value of food by *burning* it.

The Digestive System

The Breaking Down of Food

1) One of the purposes of the digestive system is to break down food. _Where_ is food first broken down? _Describe_ how is it broken down. What else happens to food here?

2) _You may be asked_ to identify different types of teeth. The diagram to the right shows the four main types of teeth. The names, pictures and functions are muddled up. Copy the diagrams and label each tooth with the _correct name_ and _correct function_. Explain how the _shape_ of each tooth fits its function.

| Molar | Incisor | Canine | Premolar |

| Biting and tearing | Grinding up hard food | Cutting | Grinding up soft food |

3) The diagrams below show the major parts of the digestive system. **D** shows the mouth, salivary glands and the oesophagus. _Identify_ the labelled parts, and write down their _letter_ and _name_.

A   B   C   D   E   F   G

The Food Route

4) These are the parts of the digestive system that food actually goes through. _Match_ each part to its correct function:

Part of digestive system   →   Function

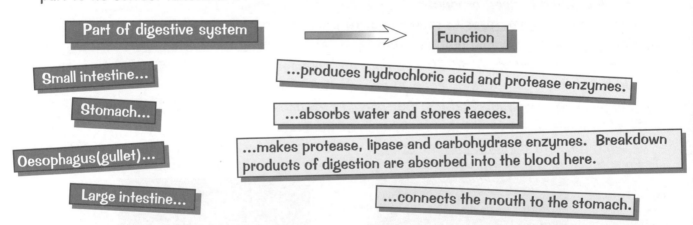

Small intestine...   ...produces hydrochloric acid and protease enzymes.

Stomach...   ...absorbs water and stores faeces.

Oesophagus(gullet)...   ...makes protease, lipase and carbohydrase enzymes. Breakdown products of digestion are absorbed into the blood here.

Large intestine...   ...connects the mouth to the stomach.

Write down the parts of the digestive system with their function in the order they would work to digest some food.

5) a) Which parts of the digestive system does food _not_ pass through?
b) Which parts of the digestive system are _muscular_?

6) _The list_ below gives four words which all end in "_-tion_". _Explain_ what each word means and put them in the correct order, starting with ingestion.

digestion   egestion   absorption   ingestion

7) Not all animals have a digestive system like ours. The starfish can digest small prey in its stomach inside its body. However, for something big the starfish turns its stomach inside out and, placing itself over its food, secretes digestive juices and absorbs the result. What are the _advantages_ and _disadvantages_ of the digestive system of the _starfish_? What are the _advantages_ of having a digestive system _like ours_ in which all the enzymes, body parts and activities are kept on the _inside_?

The Digestive System

Swallowing Food

8) *Sometimes when we eat, the food "goes down the wrong way", and we end up coughing. What is the "wrong way"? What is the "right way"? What makes food go down the "right way"?*

9) Look at the diagram below. It shows a food bolus moving through the inside of the oesophagus.

Bolus moving

a) What is a *bolus*?

b) The labels A and B point to two types of muscle. *Name* A and B.

c) What is the name given to the *muscular process* that forces food through the oesophagus and intestines?

d) *Explain* how the mechanism named in **c)** works. Mention *muscles* in your answer.

The Stomach

10) *The stomach produces hydrochloric acid and protease enzymes. What else does the stomach do to help digest food?*

11) *The internal surface of the small intestine has around five million finger-like projections, each about 1mm long.*

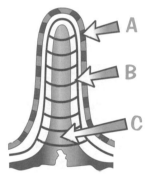

a) What are these *"fingers"* called?

b) *The diagram on the right shows one of these "fingers". Copy the diagram and name the parts labelled A, B and C.*

c) What is the advantage of *not* having a smooth internal surface in the small intestine?

d) In adults, the small intestine can be up to 6m long, and the large intestine 1.5m long. *How* do they fit inside the body and why are they so long?

Who are We?

12) We are parts of the digestive system that food does not go through. *Who are we?*

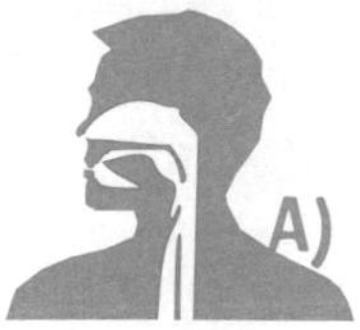

A)

A) comes in a three. "We produce saliva and amylase" — something you'll find easy to swallow.

Not everybody's favourite school meal, B) produces bile.
"I can also store excess sugar as glycogen, and remove poisons like alcohol from the blood",

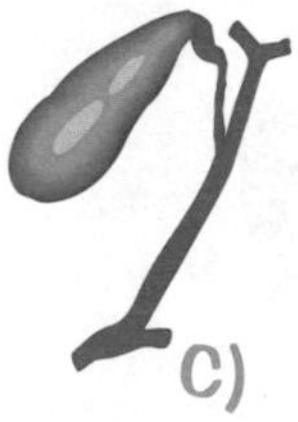

B)

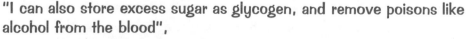

C) says "I store bile before releasing it into the small intestine".

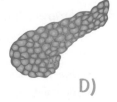

C)

D) is a rippled gland, often confused in examinations with a London railway station. Clearly upset, D) says "I produce lipase, carbohydrase and protease enzymes, not trains".

D)

Work out the true identities of A, B, C and D.

Top Tips: It would waste too much time in an exam to ask you to *draw* the digestive system — but you *will* be asked to label a diagram, so you do need to know the *whole thing*. Remember how the *structures* of the parts help them do their jobs efficiently. There's a lot of *muscle* involved, so learn where it is and what it's doing, and don't forget that lovely word *"bolus"*.

Digestive Enzymes

Catalysts and Enzymes

1) What is a _catalyst_? What is an _enzyme_?

2) What is _digestion_? What are _digestive_ enzymes?

3) You _need to know_ about three types of digestive enzymes. In the table below, the _names_ of these enzymes, the _substances_ they digest and the _products_ that are made have all been muddled up. _Write down_ the correct sentence for each enzyme.

carbohydrase		protein		fatty acids and glycerol
protease	catalyses the breakdown of	fat	into	sugar (maltose)
lipase		starch		amino acids

4) _The pH of the digestive system is very important for the functioning of digestive enzymes. For practice, copy and complete this diagram with the correct pH numbers in the boxes:_

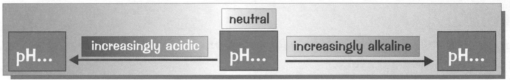

5) _Chewing gum increases the flow of saliva. The graph on the right shows the effect on the pH in the mouth when chewing gum after a meal. What does the graph tell you about saliva?_

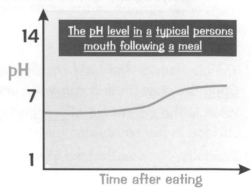

The pH level in a typical persons mouth following a meal

The Stomach

6) _Gastric juice is added to food when it reaches the stomach. This juice contains an acid._

a) Name the _acid_ secreted by the stomach.

b) _Estimate_ the pH of the _stomach_ contents, and give a reason for your answer.

c) Give two reasons _why_ the stomach secretes this acid.

7) When food reaches the small intestine from the stomach, _pancreatic juice_ and _bile_ are added to it. These substances contain a weak alkali called _sodium hydrogencarbonate_. What effect will the sodium hydrogencarbonate have on the _pH_ of the intestinal contents?

8) Describe the _changes_ in pH as food starts in the mouth, goes to the stomach and passes into the small intestine. Make sure you name the _substances_ involved in the pH changes.

9) _Enzymes have their maximum activity at an optimum pH. If the pH of their environment is too acidic or too alkaline their structure is damaged and they become denatured. The graph opposite shows the effect of pH on the activity of two protease enzymes._

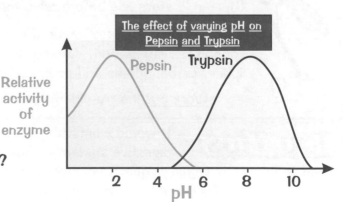

The effect of varying pH on Pepsin and Trypsin

a) What is the _optimum_ pH for each enzyme?

b) Suggest _where_ in the digestive system each enzyme would work best.

Digestive Enzymes

Digestive System

10) _Use the diagram_ below to answer the following questions.

salivary glands	oesophagus	stomach	small intestine	liver	pancreas	gall bladder	large intestine

a) Which parts of the digestive system listed above produce _carbohydrase enzymes_?
b) Where in the digestive system is _starch_ digested by carbohydrase enzymes?
c) What is likely to _prevent_ digestion of starch by carbohydrase enymes _in the stomach_?
d) Which parts of the digestive system produce _protease enzymes_?
e) Where in the digestive system is _protein_ digested by protease enzymes?
f) Which parts of the digestive system produce _lipase enzymes_?
g) Where in the digestive system is _fat_ digested by lipase enzymes?

11) _It is difficult for lipase to digest fat. Enzymes work in solution, but fat does not dissolve in water. If fat can be broken up into smaller droplets, lipase can digest the fat more effectively._

a) _Bile_ emulsifies fat. What does _emulsify_ mean?
b) What happens to the surface area of fat when it is _emulsified_?
c) Explain why bile allows lipase to _digest_ fats more effectively.

Digestive Flow Chart

12) The diagram to the right is a _flow chart_ for digestion.

Copy the diagram. Use your answers to Question 10) **a)** to **g)** to _complete_ it.

Your finished flow chart should show _where_ each digestive enzyme is produced, and _where_ each nutrient is digested.

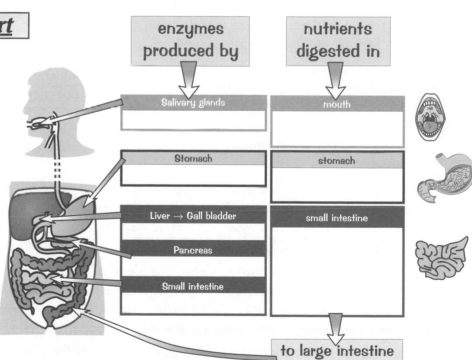

enzymes produced by

nutrients digested in

Salivary glands

mouth

Stomach

stomach

Liver → Gall bladder

small intestine

Pancreas

Small intestine

to large intestine

13) _Describe_ in words what happens to food after it enters the body. Mention _where_ the nutrients are being digested, the names of the _nutrients_, the names of the _digestive enzymes_ and where they are produced, and the _products of digestion_.

Top Tips: There's a lot to learn on these pages, including some ace _strange long names_. Don't be tempted to cut corners, because you really need to learn all this stuff. Go through it bit by bit, and remember where the enzymes are _made_, where they _act_, and what the nutrients are _broken down into_. Don't forget that each enzyme works best at an optimum _temperature_ and _pH_, and that digestion happens _faster_ if there is a _large surface area_ for the enzymes to work on.

Absorption of Food

Absorption of Nutrients

1) *Match* each nutrient to its correct form when digested:

starch is digested to form ...

protein is digested to form ...

fat is digested to form ...

... smaller molecules called fatty acids and glycerol

... smaller molecules called sugars

... smaller molecules called amino acids

Separation Techniques

2) *A student was given a mixture of sand and sugar in a beaker. He was asked to separate the sand from the sugar. He decided to use the method shown in the diagrams opposite.*

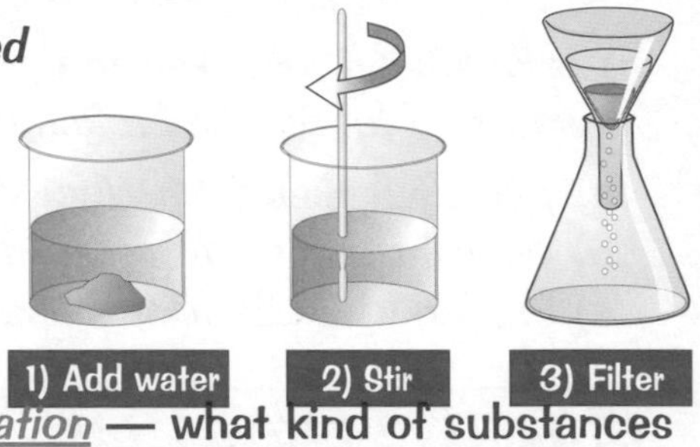

a) What happens to the <u>sand</u> when the mixture is <u>stirred</u>?
b) What happens to the <u>sugar</u> when the mixture is <u>stirred</u>?
c) What happens to the <u>sand</u> when the mixture is <u>filtered</u>?
d) What happens to the <u>sugar</u> when the mixture is <u>filtered</u>?

1) Add water   2) Stir   3) Filter

e) Look at your answers so far. Explain what we mean by <u>filtration</u> — what kind of substances can be filtered and what kind cannot?

3) *Make a table* like the one below.

soluble	insoluble

a) Put the substances in the box below into the <u>correct columns</u> in the table:

| amino acids | <u>fat</u> | <u>protein</u> | <u>glycerol</u> |
| <u>starch</u> | <u>sugar</u> | <u>fatty acids</u> | |

b) Which of these substances could be <u>separated</u> from water using filter paper? <u>Explain</u> your answer.
c) What is <u>wrong</u> with the idea that the products of digestion are "filtered into the blood"?

Changing the Rates of Absorption

4) *The rate of movement of sugars through a piece of intestine wall was measured. This was done for four sugars (glucose, A, B and C). Then some cyanide was added to the piece of intestine (this stops respiration in the cells, and so stops any process that needs energy). The rates of movement were measured again. The results are shown below.*

a) Which two sugars moved <u>fastest</u> through the wall of the intestine?

b) Which two sugars moved <u>slowest</u> through the wall of the intestine?

c) Why does adding <u>cyanide</u> have little or no effect on the rate of movement of sugars B and C? What <u>process</u> is being used to move these sugars through the wall of the intestine?

d) Why does <u>adding</u> cyanide have such a dramatic effect on the rate of movement of glucose and A? What <u>additional process</u> is also working to move these sugars through the wall?

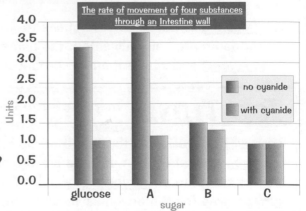

SECTION THREE — HUMAN BIOLOGY PART ONE

Absorption of Food

The Movement of Nutrients

5) A student did an experiment to show the movement of nutrients through the walls of a model intestine. She made a watertight bag using Visking tubing, which is partially permeable. She put a mixture of starch suspension and sugar solution into the bag, and put the bag into a boiling tube containing distilled water (see diagram). At the beginning of the experiment she tested the contents of the bag and the water for starch and sugar. She did this again after 30 minutes. Her results are shown in the table.

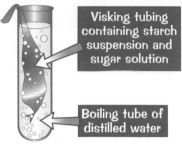

Visking tubing containing starch suspension and sugar solution

Boiling tube of distilled water

time (minutes)	contents of bag		water	
	starch	sugar	starch	sugar
0	✔	✔	✘	✘
30	✔	✔	✘	✔

a) How did _sugar_ get into the tube of water during the experiment?

b) Why was there _no starch_ in the water at the end of the experiment?

c) Suggest _three_ ways that the student could _speed up_ the process described in your answer to part a)

The Digestive System

6) The products of digestion are absorbed into the bloodstream.

a) In _which part_ of the digestive system does this happen?

b) Is _dietary fibre_ absorbed?

c) The various digestive juices add greatly to the volume of water taken in by eating and drinking. In _which part_ of the digestive system is _excess water_ absorbed?

d) What other _function_ does this part of the digestive system have?

e) What do you think will happen if _too much_ water is absorbed?

f) What will happen if _too little_ water is absorbed?

Diffusion

7) The following passage is about diffusion.

a) Choose the _correct words_ from the underlined pairs and copy it out:

"Diffusion is the _active_ / _passive_ movement of particles _up_ / _down_ a concentration gradient from a _high_ / _low_ concentration to a _high_ / _low_ concentration. Diffusion through membranes is _faster_ / _slower_ when the membrane is thin and has a _small_ / _large_ surface area."

b) _Explain how_ the structure of the small intestine allows for the efficient movement of the products of digestion through its wall. Include the words _"villi"_ and _"epithelium"_ in your answer. _A labelled diagram may help_.

c) _Explain how_ the structure of the small intestine allows for the rapid absorption of the products of digestion into the bloodstream. Include the word _capillaries_ in your answer.

Top Tips: Get that extra mark in the exam by using the word _"absorb"_. If you know that protein is digested into amino acids (small soluble molecules) why _spoil_ it all by writing _"protein is filtered into the blood"_? Better to write that, _"in the small intestine amino acids are absorbed into the bloodstream"_. Remember that _diffusion_ from high concentration to low concentration _doesn't_ need energy, but going from low concentration to high concentration _does_. Also, don't forget that molecules can't diffuse into the blood if they're _too big_.

SECTION THREE — HUMAN BIOLOGY PART ONE

Deficiency Diseases

The Need for Minerals

1) a) _Copy_ these sentences about minerals, choosing the correct words from the _underlined pairs_.

> _Iron_ / _calcium_ is needed to make the haemoglobin found in red blood cells.

> _Iron_ / _calcium_ is needed to maintain strong bones and teeth.

b) *About 90% of the calcium stored in our body is found in bone.*
   What happens if we have too little calcium in our diet?

c) Explain why food manufacturers put _calcium carbonate_ and _iron sulphate_ into flour.

2) *It has been estimated that 2 billion people have iron deficiency. The majority of these are women.*

a) Name the disease caused by a _deficiency of iron_ in a persons diet, suggest the likely symptoms.

b) Suggest a reason _why_ the majority of people with iron deficiency are women.

c) *Intestinal parasites feed on the blood of the infected host. Some parasites, such as _Schistosoma haematobium_, cause blood to come out in the urine. In Third World countries, these infections make the symptoms of iron deficiency worse. _Suggest why_ .*

d) *Medicine to kill intestinal worms in a person costs about 2p a dose. This is not very expensive, but how much would it cost to treat all the people who have iron deficiency? _Discuss_ whether this would be an effective solution to iron deficiency. Would there be any other benefits?*

e) What _improvements_ to the diet could be made to eliminate iron deficiency?

f) What problems might there be in Third World countries of trying to improve the _diet_ in the way suggested in your answer to part e)?

Iodine Deficiency

3) _Read_ the information below about iodine deficiency, then _answer the questions_.

The average intelligence quotient (IQ) is 100, but iodine deficiency can reduce your IQ by up to 10 points. Significant iodine deficiency can cause brain damage. The most obvious symptom of iodine deficiency is goitre. In this disease, the thyroid gland enlarges, causing the front of the neck to swell up, and the gland may have to be removed by surgery.

Following a study on iodine deficiency and goitre, a goitre prevention programme using iodised salt started in America in 1924. Salt producers sold iodised and plain salt at the same price, and newspapers urged people to use iodised salt to prevent iodine deficiency. As a result, household use of iodised salt eliminated iodine deficiency in America.

Iodine can be added to salt as potassium iodide or potassium iodate. Potassium iodate is more stable than potassium iodide in hot, humid conditions. Globally, 750 million people have goitre caused by iodine deficiency, but the numbers are falling. In 1990, 120,000 babies were born cretins (severely iodine deficient, and as adults they might only have the intelligence of a four-year-old). In 1997, 45% of this number were born cretins.

a) What are the _symptoms_ of mild and severe iodine deficiency?

b) What _steps_ were taken to ensure that the American programme to iodise salt was successful?

c) *In 1990, a World Summit for Children singled out iodine deficiency as one of three deficiencies to eliminate by 2000. _Suggest why_ this was one of the targets set.*

d) _Work out_ how many babies were born cretins as a result of iodine deficiency in 1997.

e) Suggest how you would successfully _iodise salt_ and encourage its use in Third World countries.

Section Three — Human Biology Part One

Deficiency Diseases

Problems associated with Poor Diets

4) Minerals need to be in solution to be absorbed by the intestine. Some foods such as cereals and wholemeal bread contain a substance called phytic acid. This can form insoluble salts of calcium and iron. _What problem_ could eating an excess of phytic acid cause?

5) Kwashiorkor is a disease caused by too little protein in the diet. This causes the loss of body fat and the bloating of the abdomen. What other _problems_ could be caused by too little protein in the diet?

6) Look at these _extracts_ from study reports on nutrition.

> "... more than 13 million children under five years old in poor families in country X are hungry for one or more months a year. Over 15% of them do not get enough calcium, and 25% of them did not get enough iron ..."
>
> "... In country Y, the diet of poor families tends to be low in essential nutrients like calcium, iron and vitamin C. They do not eat enough fruit, vegetables and wholemeal bread ..."
>
> "... in country Z, poor families spend over 25% of their income on food, but eat a similar diet to the one eaten by poor families in country Y..."

These countries are not in the Third World. Country X is the USA, country Y is the UK, and country Z is France. _Discuss_, in the form of a short essay, the _implications_ that these findings will have on the governments and health authorities in these countries. Also think about the implications of your choice of foods (do you get _enough_ essential nutrients — do _you_ choose crisps instead of an apple?)

Vitamin Deficiencies

7) Linus Pauling, the second person to win a Nobel Prize twice (Marie Curie was the first person), believed that massive doses of vitamin C would prevent illnesses such as colds and 'flu. However, this has not been proved by experiments. Vitamin C is soluble in water, and unused vitamin C can leave the body quickly.
   a) Suggest _how_ unused vitamin C might leave the body quickly.
   b) When cooking vegetables, why is microwaving them often considered to be _"healthier"_ than boiling them in a pan of water?

8) Vitamin D deficiency causes rickets. Too much vitamin D in the diet can cause kidney damage, tiredness, and loss of appetite.
   a) What are the symptoms of _rickets_?
   b) Vitamin D is often called the "sunshine vitamin". Why?
   c) Vitamin D is soluble in fat, not in water. To increase the amount of vitamin D in the diet, manufacturers add vitamin D to some foods as a nutritional supplement. _Suggest_ a food that could have vitamin D _added_ to it.
   d) Vitamin D can be stored in the body. Suggest where the body might _store_ vitamin D.

9) Sailors who spent months at sea without fresh fruit and vegetables suffered from a disease caused by vitamin C deficiency. This was often fatal. In 1795, a Scottish doctor called James Lind recommended that lime juice should be given to sailors on British naval vessels, and the disease soon began to disappear among British sailors.
   a) What disease is caused by _vitamin C deficiency_?
   b) What are the _symptoms_ of this disease?
   c) Suggest _another way_ that this disease could be avoided.

Top Tips:
You know _why_ we need the various nutrients — so now think what would happen if we _didn't_ get them in our diet. Be ready to _describe_ the effects of lacking _protein_, _iron_, _calcium_, and vitamins _C_ and _D_. One gruesome effect of each deficiency, accurately recalled, will do.

Food Tests

Testing for Sugar Content

1) *Benedict's reagent can be used to detect reducing sugars. Most sugars, such as glucose and maltose, are reducing sugars. Some, such as sucrose, are not. Water is added to a sample of food in a test tube to help dissolve the sugars. Benedict's reagent is then added, and the mixture is heated in a water bath for several minutes. If enough reducing sugar is present, the mixture goes cloudy and there are several colour changes until the final colour is reached. Some of these colours are shown in the table on the right, but the starting and finishing colours have been left out.*

   a) <u>Copy</u> and <u>complete</u> the table.

If there is not enough sugar in the food sample, the later colour changes do not happen. Angela tested two foods using Benedict's reagent. Food A produced a cloudy brown colour after a few minutes; food B produced a cloudy green colour after a few minutes.

colour at start	?
↓	cloudy green
	cloudy yellow
	cloudy brown
colour at end	?

   b) Which food probably contained the <u>highest</u> concentration of sugar?

   c) *Angela was not sure that her experiment was a fair test, and thought that there could be another explanation for her results. Suggest <u>another explanation</u> for Angela's results, and suggest what she could do to <u>improve</u> her experiment to make it a fair test.*

Angela improved her experiment, and tested lots of different sugars provided by her teacher. One of the sugars gave no colour change at all, however much Benedicts reagent she crammed into the test tube.

   d) Why did one of the sugars give <u>no colour change</u>.

   e) Suggest the <u>name</u> of this sugar.

Iodine Detection

2) *Iodine occurs as a shiny black solid at room temperature which can easily turn into a purple vapour. When dissolved in water with a little potassium iodide, iodine forms a brown solution.*

   a) What type of <u>nutrient</u> can be detected using iodine solution?

   b) What colour change happens when <u>iodine</u> solution is <u>added</u> to this type of nutrient?

An Experiment using Amylase

3) *Iqbal wanted to see if the amylase in his saliva could digest starch to sugar. His teacher wasn't keen on the class spitting, even in the name of science, and supplied some ready-made amylase instead. He set up the experiment shown on the right.*

mixture of starch suspension and amylase

beaker of warm water

   a) What should Iqbal see when he tests a sample of the starting mixture with <u>iodine solution</u>? Explain why he should get this result.

   b) *After 20 minutes, Iqbal tested the mixture with Benedict's reagent. It turned red. What does this result <u>mean</u>?*

   c) *Iqbal's teacher wasn't sure that the experiment showed that starch had been digested to sugar. Two important tests had been missed out. What were these <u>missing</u> tests? What results would you expect to see if the starch <u>had been digested</u> to sugar?*

   d) *Iqbal repeated the experiment, and included the two missing tests. Unfortunately, his teacher was not convinced that the experiment showed that amylase was needed to digest starch. What <u>control experiment</u> should have been set up?*

SECTION THREE — HUMAN BIOLOGY PART ONE

Food Tests

Biuret and Emulsion Tests

4) Paul has lost his instructions for the biuret food test. He can remember bits of it, but isn't sure of the details. He has written down as much as he can remember, but there are gaps. *Copy* John's instructions (on the right), *replacing* the dodgy splodges with the *correct* words.

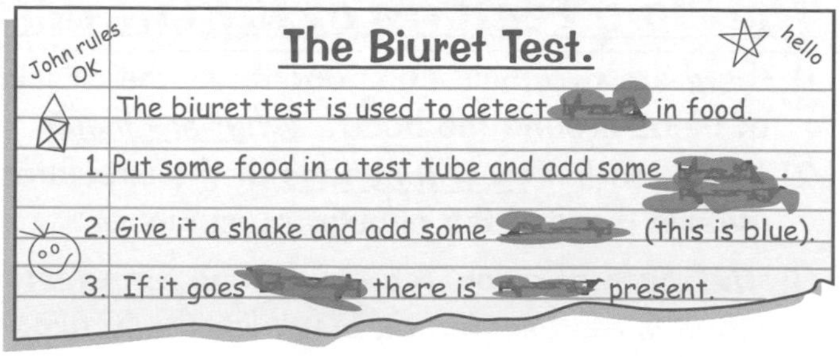

> **The Biuret Test.** ☆ hello
> John rules OK
> The biuret test is used to detect ▓▓▓▓ in food.
> 1. Put some food in a test tube and add some ▓▓▓▓.
> 2. Give it a shake and add some ▓▓▓▓ (this is blue).
> 3. If it goes ▓▓▓▓ there is ▓▓▓▓ present.

5) Fats can be detected using the emulsion test. Food is put in a test tube and ethanol is added. The test tube is shaken, some water is added, and the tube is shaken again.

 a) If *fat* is present in the food, what would you expect to see happen?
 b) Why is *ethanol* added to the food? Why is the tube *shaken* after the ethanol is added?
 c) Why is the tube shaken after adding *water* to it?
 d) What *safety precautions* should be taken when doing a test like this?

6) Ruso has been eating potato crisps while doing her homework. Some bits of crisp have fallen on the book. She brushed the bits of crisp off the book, but they left behind some clear, translucent stains on the page. Keen to investigate, she found that cake crumbs did the same thing, but dry toast crumbs did not. What type of *nutrient* in the food was responsible for leaving the spot on the page? What experiment could you do to *support* your answer?

A Jam-Making Experiment

7) If you want to make home-made jam, you have to boil sugar (sucrose) with fruit. The acids in the fruit react with the sucrose, and turn it into a mixture of glucose and fructose. This mixture of sugars is called "invert sugar". Invert sugar is much less likely than sucrose to crystallise when cool, so it gives nice smooth jam.

 a) Explain the results you would expect if you tested *sucrose* with Benedict's reagent.
 b) Explain the results you would expect if you tested the *invert sugar* with Benedict's reagent.
 c) Describe how you could use Benedict's reagent to monitor your jam-making process so that you could produce some nice jam.

The chemicals used in the biuret test react with the chemical bonds between the amino acids in the protein. If there are only a few bonds, such as in a molecule made of few amino acids, you get a pale pink colour. If there are a lot of bonds such as in a protein, you get a purple colour.

 d) Describe how you could *modify* your answer to part **c)** to monitor the digestion of egg-white protein to amino acids by a protease enzyme.

8) *Summarise* your knowledge of food tests by drawing up a table with the headings shown on the right. *Complete* your table with the food tests and results expected for *starch*, *sugars*, *proteins* and *fats*.

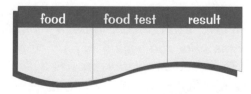

food	food test	result

Circulatory System

The Main Features of the Circulatory System

1) There are two main components of the circulatory system which maintain a continuous flow of blood around the body. _What are they_?

2) What are the _main functions_ of the circulatory system?
   Why is it called the circulatory system?

3) _The diagram below represents the main features of the circulatory system. Deoxygenated blood is represented by black lines, and oxygenated blood by white lines. The arrows show the direction of movement._
   Using your knowledge and the clues in the diagram below, _match_ the blood vessels labelled 1 — 5 and the organs labelled A — D to their correct names in the table.

Blood vessels	Number	Organs	Letter
Pulmonary vein		Intestines	
Hepatic vein		Kidneys	
Renal artery		Liver	
Aorta		Lungs	
Vena cava			

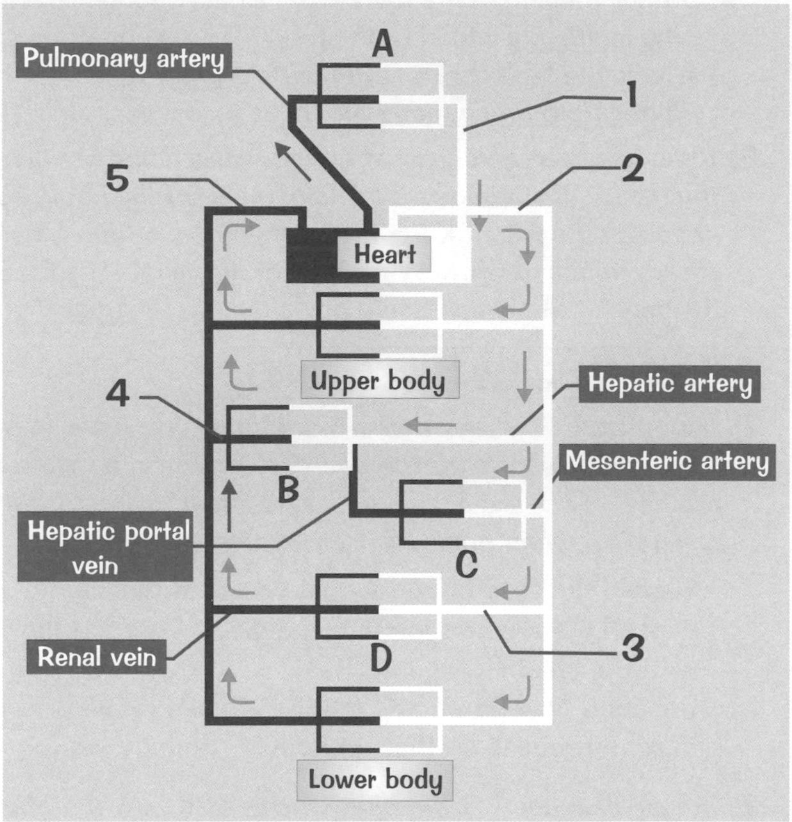

4) _After the pulmonary artery leaves the heart, it branches into two (although this is not shown in the diagram)._
   Why does it do this?

5) From the _evidence_ in the diagram, and from what you have learnt so far what is the _difference_ between an artery and a vein?
   Name the vein which _doesn't_ go directly back to the heart.

Diagram labels: Pulmonary artery, A, 1, 5, 2, Heart, Upper body, Hepatic artery, 4, Mesenteric artery, B, Hepatic portal vein, C, Renal vein, D, 3, Lower body

Parasitic Infection

6) _Schistosomiasis is a disease caused by a parasitic trematode worm. The adult parasite lives inside the hepatic portal vein and the blood vessels surrounding the intestine, where it feeds on blood. The parasite, which takes about six weeks to grow to its adult length of about 1cm, infects around 200 million people in the tropics._

   Infection starts when you bathe in an infected river or irrigation canal. The larva senses human skin, and burrows through it in a few seconds. It then works its way into a blood vessel under the skin, and begins its journey to the liver and intestine, growing and feeding as it does this. The blood circulation pushes it along.

   a) _Essie has just been infected by the parasite after fetching water from an infected river. The larva has burrowed into the soft skin between her toes. _Describe_ by drawing a flow diagram the shortest journey the larva could take on its way to the blood vessels in Essie's liver. _Make sure_ that you mention the _names_ of organs and major blood vessels visited by the parasite._

   b) _Sometimes, the larva is too small to stay in the blood vessels of the liver and intestine, and gets pushed straight through them. Luckily for them, but not for Essie, they still get another chance to get there. _Why is this_?_

Circulatory System

Blood Flow Problems

7) Mr Spanner is happily washing his car using a garden hose, then one of his children stands on the hose as a practical joke.
   a) What happens to the _diameter_ of the hose where the child is standing on it?
   b) What happens to the _flow_ of water from the hose?
   c) Water begins to leak from the connection of the hose to the garden tap. _Why_?
   d) Mr Spanner's garden hose is only about 1cm in diameter, but the Fire Brigade uses really wide hoses for putting out fires. What _advantage_ does the Fire Brigade get from using such hoses?
   e) Our blood vessels are a bit like Mr Spanner's garden hose. They carry a fluid, blood, around the body. _What_ would happen to the flow of blood in an _artery_ if it became narrow at one point? _What_ would happen to the blood pressure in the section _before_ the narrow point?

8) The diagrams on the right show a section of healthy artery, and a section of diseased artery.
   a) _Describe_ the _difference_ between the two sections.
   b) What will happen to the flow of blood through the _diseased artery_?
   c) What effect will the changes in the diseased artery have on the _blood pressure_?

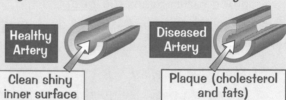

Healthy Artery — Clean shiny inner surface

Diseased Artery — Plaque (cholesterol and fats)

   Cholesterol is important for the correct functioning of our bodies. For example, it is used in cell membranes and to make vitamin D. The liver can make cholesterol, but most comes from the diet. Too much cholesterol in a persons diet can lead to the deposit of fatty deposits in artieries.

   d) Which _foods_ should you cut down on to _reduce_ the amount of cholesterol in your diet?
   e) If the artery became completely _blocked_, what would happen to the flow of blood to the _tissues_ supplied by that artery? _Explain_ what would happen to the _cells_ in those tissues.
   f) The plaque coating the inside of the artery can break off and block blood vessels. Blood clots can do this too. Such blockage is called a _thrombosis_. What happens if there is a thrombosis in the _coronary artery_? What happens if there is one in a _blood vessel_ in the _brain_?

9) The smooth muscle in the walls of the arteries can contract, especially when you are under stress.
   a) What is the effect on the _diameter_ of the arteries when these smooth muscles _contract_?
   b) Is this process called vasodilation _or_ vasoconstriction?
   c) Suggest the likely _effects_ on the circulatory system as a result of _prolonged stress_.

How Exercise Affects the Pulse Rate

10) Mr Spanner's car broke down, and he had to push it. The table shows what happened to his heart when he did this exercise.

	At rest	Pushing Car
Heart rate (beats per minute)	60	150
Stroke volume (cm³)	100	120
Cardiac Output (cm³ per minute)	6000	18000

   a) What is the effect of _exercise_ on the heart rate and stroke volume (volume pumped in one beat)?

   b) _Study the table carefully_. What _cardiac output_ would you expect if Mr Spanner had a heart rate of 100 beats per minute and a stroke volume of 110cm³? Show your working out clearly.
   c) Why do we need an _increased_ cardiac output when we exercise?
   d) _Fit_ athletes often have very _low_ resting heart rates. Suggest a reason _why_.

Top Tips:
Plenty of facts on these pages, and you really need to learn them to get to grips with what the circulation system does. Be prepared to _name_ the blood vessels in diagrams — so learn those odd names . Don't forget that the human circulation system is a _double_ circulation system — one loop goes to the _lungs_ to _collect oxygen_, and the _other_ loop goes _around the body_. You need to be able to describe how the _heart_ is affected by _exercise_.

The Heart

How the Heart Works

1) The diagram on the right shows the human heart as a simple engineering drawing viewed from the front, rather than as a cross-section of a real heart.

   Black arrows show the movement of deoxygenated blood, and the white arrows show the movement of oxygenated blood. Valves are shaded in grey.

   a) How many _chambers_ are there in the heart?

   b) What are the _upper chambers_ called?

   c) What are the _lower chambers_ called?

   d) To which _side_ of the heart does deoxygenated blood return from the _body_?

   e) To which side of the heart does _oxygenated_ blood return from the _lungs_?

   f) There are _four_ valves in the heart. What is their function?

   g) The valve labelled **X** is called the tricuspid valve, and the valve labelled **Y** is called the bicuspid valve. Suggest a _reason_ for these names.

   h) What is the _name_ of the other two valves?

   i) The heart forms two pumps. What does _each_ pump do?

The different Parts of the Heart

2) You may be asked to label the components of the heart. The diagram on the right represents a cross-section of the human heart drawn from the front. _Identify_ each of the parts labelled A — G. (Your answers to question 1 should help you to do this.) _Make a table_ to show your answers.

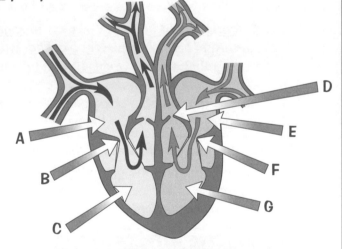

label	part of heart

3) You may also be asked to label the blood vessels going into and out of the heart. The diagram on the right represents a cross-section of the human heart drawn from the front. _Identify_ each of the blood vessels labelled 1 — 4.

   Make a table to show your answers.

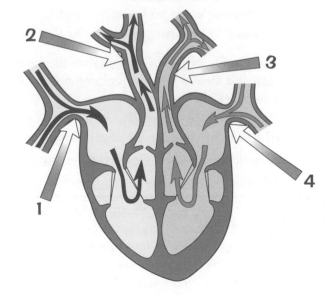

label	blood vessel

The Heart

How the Heart Functions

4) Match each _blood vessel_ to its correct _function_:

the vena cava...   ...carries oxygenated blood to the rest of the body

the pulmonary vein...   ...carries deoxygenated blood to the lungs

the pulmonary artery...   ...carries oxygenated blood away from the lungs

the aorta...   ...carries deoxygenated blood to the heart

5) _The walls of the left side of the heart are generally thicker than those of the right side of the heart, and the walls of the ventricles are thicker than those of the atria._

    a) Suggest _reasons_ for these differences.

    b) _What type_ of tissue are the walls of the heart made from? _Explain_ how you could work this out from your knowledge of the action of the heart.

    c) _The word "coronary" means something to do with the heart._ What do the coronary _arteries_ do? What do the coronary _veins_ do?

    d) _Explain_ what could happen to the heart if a clot or a fatty plaque _blocked_ a coronary artery.

    e) _Some babies are born with an abnormal opening joining their two ventricles. This is often called "blue baby syndrome" because their skin has a bluish tinge._ Suggest a reason _why_ their skin looks this colour.

6) _Look at the sentences below._ They all describe the way in which the right side of the heart pumps blood received from the body to the lungs. To make things tricky, they are muddled up.

The atrium contracts to finish filling the ventricle with blood.

The semi-lunar valves stop blood flowing backwards into the ventricle.

The tricuspid valve shuts to stop blood going back into the atrium.

The walls of the ventricle push the blood out of the heart through the pulmonary artery.

The ventricle contracts, squeezing the blood inside.

The vena cava brings blood from the body to the heart.

While the right ventricle is relaxed, blood flows into it through the open tricuspid valve.

Blood pours into the right atrium.

    a) _Write down_ the sentences in the correct order, _starting with_ "_The vena cava brings blood from the body to the heart_" and _finishing with_ "_The semi-lunar valves stop blood flowing backwards into the ventricle_".

    b) _Work out_ what must happen when the left side of the heart pumps blood received from the lungs to the rest of the body. _Write down_ your answer with the same amount of detail as part **a)**.

    c) Look at your answers to parts **a)** and **b)**. _What events_ are common to the working of both sides of the heart? Draw a _flow chart_ to show these common events in the correct order.

Top Tips: Obviously, the heart is kind of important. It's a _double pump_, and you need to remember why. You've really got to learn the diagram of the heart, because _almost without doubt_ you will be asked to label one in the Exam — don't forget, it's drawn from the front, so the right side is on the left of the page — I suppose you'll _know it all back-to-front_. You need to know what the _valves_ are for, _where_ the _deoxygenated blood_ is and which side is _bigger_.

SECTION THREE — HUMAN BIOLOGY PART ONE

Blood Vessels

Understanding Blood Vessels

1) _Two_ sentences can be made from the one below by choosing the correct words from the pairs. _Find them both_:

"_Arteries_ /_veins_ carry blood _to_ /_from_ the heart at _low_ /_high_ pressure"

Characteristics of Arteries and Veins

2) The diagrams below show _cross-sections_ of arteries and veins. They are _not_ drawn to scale.

   a) _Copy_ the diagrams and fill in the _missing labels_.

   b) Describe the _similarities_ and _differences_ between the cross-sections of arteries and veins.

   c) _Explain_ how each blood vessel is _adapted_ for its function. Your correct answer to question 1) should help you.

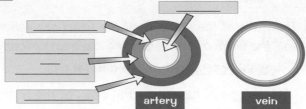

3) The diagrams on the right show pieces of artery and vein sliced _along their length_. They are not drawn to scale.

   a) _Copy_ the diagrams with the correct names of the blood vessels.

   b) What is the name of the _extra_ structure in diagram A?

   c) What is the _function_ of this structure?

   d) _Where else_ in the circulatory system can these structures be found?

   e) Work out which way the blood must be flowing in vessel A and add an _arrow_ to your diagram to show the _direction_ of blood flow. _Explain how_ you worked this out.

   f) What keeps the blood moving in vessel A?

   g) What keeps the blood moving in vessel B?

   h) Look at your answers to parts f) and g). _What type_ of tissue is common to both answers?

Capillaries

4) _Arteries divide into narrower arterioles, which then divide into even smaller vessels, called capillaries (see diagram). These form dense networks between cells in tissues and organs._

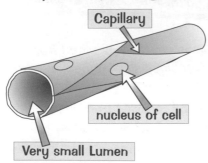

Capillary

nucleus of cell

Very small Lumen

   a) Although capillaries join arteries and veins together this is not their function. What is their _function_?

   b) How does the structure of the _capillary wall_ allow it to carry out this function effectively?

   c) _Red blood cells_ are about 7.5μm (μm = thousandth of a metre) in diameter. What would you expect the diameter of the _narrowest_ capillary to be? _Explain_ your answer.

5) In which type of blood vessel do we find our _pulse_?

   Why can't we detect a pulse in the other _2 types_ of blood vessel?

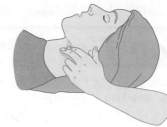

SECTION THREE — HUMAN BIOLOGY PART ONE

The Blood

1) The main components of blood are red cells, platelets, white cells and plasma. There are about 5 litres of blood in an average adult. We can take a test tube of blood, and put it in a centrifuge. A centrifuge works a bit like a spin drier, and pulls the contents of the blood down towards the bottom of the test tube. The diagram on the right shows the sort of results you get if you do this.

   a) Layer A is a straw-coloured liquid. What is its _name_?
   b) What cells are found in layer B and C? What _else_ will be found in layer B?
   c) Looking at the diagram, _estimate_ what proportion of blood is made up of cells.

Red Blood Cells

2) There are about five million red blood cells in each 1mm³ of blood. That's a lot!
   a) What is the _function_ of _red blood cells_?
   b) Red blood cells have a shape called a _biconcave disc_ (see diagram on the right). Explain how this shape _helps_ a red blood cell to carry out its function.
   c) Name the substance contained in red blood cells which allows them to carry oxygen. How does it work?
   d) Red blood cells in humans and most other mammals have _no nucleus_. How does this feature _help_ a red blood cell carry out its function effectively?

3) If a gas fire burns without enough ventilation, a colourless, odourless gas called carbon monoxide is formed due to a shortage of oxygen. This combines more strongly with haemoglobin than oxygen does, and is difficult to split from it.
   Explain why carbon monoxide is so _dangerous_, and why gas fires should be _checked regularly_.

Platelets

4) Platelets are small fragments of cells. Like red cells, they do not have a nucleus, but they are only about a third of the size of a red cell. There is one platelet to every 12 red cells in the blood. That's a lot too. What is the _function_ of platelets?

White Blood Cells and Plasma

5) There is one white cell to every 600 red cells in the blood. That's still quite a lot! White cells are involved in protecting the body against infection, and don't just occur in the blood.

   a) _Copy_ the diagram of a white cell. _Complete_ the labels.
   b) Give _three_ ways in which white cells _protect_ us against infection.
   c) _Where else_ in the body might you find white cells?

6) Plasma is important because the red cells, platelets and white cells are suspended in it. One other important function of plasma is transport. What _substances_ does plasma transport? _Choose_ from the list below.

   hormones, oxygen, urea, antibodies, carbon dioxide, products of digestion, antitoxins, water, dissolved mineral salts.

7) _Draw a summary table_ to show the functions of each of the _four_ components of blood.

Top Tips: If you understand what the blood vessels do, you'll find it pretty easy to spot the differences between them on a diagram. Remember — _arteries_ carry blood _from_ the heart, _veins_ carry blood _towards_ the heart — whether the blood is blue or red. You need to know the _four_ main components of blood on this page — what they _look like_, and what they _do_. Don't forget, plasma sounds boring, but it carries everything our cells need except oxygen.

Lungs and Breathing

The Breathing System

1) Copy and complete the passage below about the _breathing system_, choosing the _correct words_ from the _underlined pairs_:

> "The breathing system takes _air_ / _oxygen_ into and out of the body. This allows _carbon dioxide_ / _oxygen_ to pass from the air into the bloodstream, and _carbon dioxide_ / _oxygen_ to pass out of the bloodstream into the air".

Identifying the Parts of the Thorax

2) _The diagram to the right represents the thorax._

a) Which _organ_ would normally be found in the space at X?

b) _Match_ up the letters A — K with the correct labels given below:

- alveoli
- bronchiole
- bronchus
- diaphragm
- intercostal muscles
- lung
- pleural membranes
- rib
- trachea

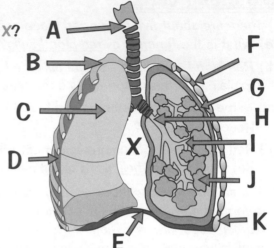

3) a) What feature of the thorax _protects_ the lungs from external damage?

b) What feature of the thorax separates the _lungs_ from the _abdomen_ (lower part of the body)?

c) What is the function of the _pleural membranes_?

The Air Passages and the Trachea

4) _When air is breathed in through the nose or mouth, it passes through parts of the breathing system to the alveoli._
Write down these parts of the breathing system in the _correct order_ :

> bronchioles   trachea   bronchi   alveoli

5) a) Give _another name_ for the trachea.

b) _The trachea has rings of cartilage around it._ What is the purpose of these?

c) The trachea splits into smaller air passages called _bronchi_ (one on its own is called a _bronchus_). _How many_ bronchi are there in each lung?

d) What is a _bronchiole_?

e) What is an _alveolus_?

Mucus and Cilia

6) _A mucus membrane and many cilia cover the inside surfaces of the air passages._

a) What does the _mucus membrane_ do? How does this help the lungs?

b) What are _cilia_? What do they do? How does this help the lungs?

7) _It has been estimated that we have about 2500km of airways in our lungs, and that the surface area of our lungs is about 40 times the surface area of our body._ _Why_ does the surface area of our lungs have to be so great? Why can't we just breathe _through_ our skin?

Lungs and Breathing

The Action of Breathing

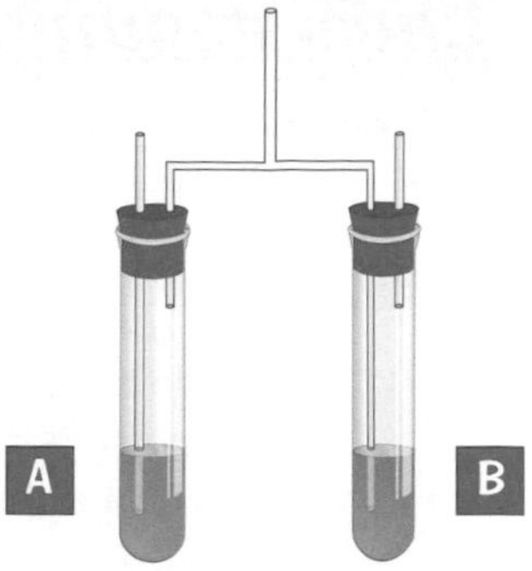

8) The apparatus shown in the diagram on the right is often used in science
   lessons to show that the gas we breathe in is different from the gas
   we breathe out. You have to breathe in and out through the top tube.

   a) Both tubes contain limewater. Which _gas_ does limewater detect?

   b) When the apparatus is used properly, which tube will contain very _cloudy_
      limewater, A or B? Explain your answer.

9) Look at the sentences below. They are all to do with movements of the
   thorax and diaphragm when we breathe in, but to make things tricky they have been muddled up.

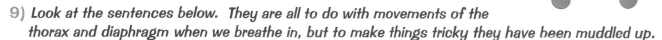

| The pressure inside the thorax gets less than atmospheric pressure. | Air is pushed into the lungs from outside to make the pressures equal. |

This pulls the ribcage upwards. | The pressure inside the thorax goes down.

This causes the diaphragm to flatten. | The diaphragm muscles contract.

The muscles between the ribs contract. | The volume of the thorax increases.

   a) Write down the sentences in the correct order, _starting_ with "The muscles between the ribs contract"
      and _finishing_ with "Air is pushed into the lungs from outside to make the pressures equal".

   b) Work out what must happen when we _breathe out_. Write down your answer with the same
      amount of detail as your answer to part **a**).

10) If you hiccup for more than 48 hours, you ought to see your doctor. Apparently, Charles
    Osbourne did a hiccup every 1½ seconds for nearly 70 years until February 1969, when he
    suddenly stopped! When you hiccup, air is inhaled very quickly.
    What must your _diaphragm_ be doing when you hiccup?

Inhalation and Exhalation

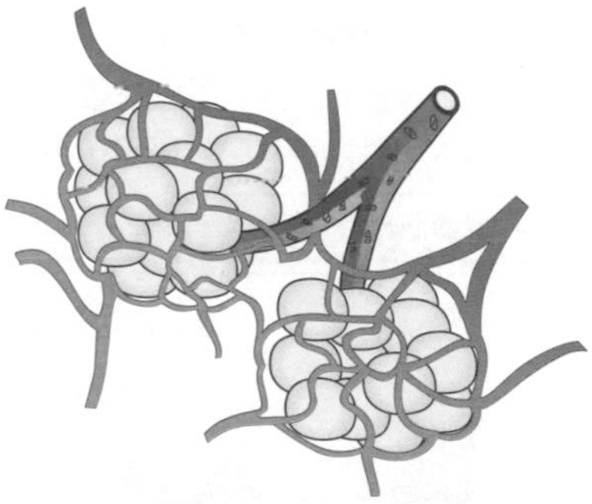

11) We each have over 300 million alveoli in the lungs. This ensures that
    we can pass enough oxygen into our bloodstream and remove the
    waste carbon dioxide from it by diffusion.

    Explain how the structure of the alveoli allows this gas exchange
    between air and blood to happen quickly.

12) The table opposite should show the approximate
    percentages of oxygen, carbon dioxide and nitrogen
    in a person's inhaled and exhaled air. _Copy_ and
    complete the table placing the muddled percentages
    provided in their correct places.
    The percentages are 0.04, 21, 78, 16, 4 and 78.

GAS	% in inhaled air	% in exhaled air
oxygen		
carbon dioxide		
nitrogen		

13) Breathing is sometimes called ventilation — not quite the same thing as leaving the window open!
    Remember that in science, respiration is not the same thing as breathing, either. The questions
    above are all about the lungs and breathing but, for practice, write down the _equation_ for respiration.

Top Tips: This is breathing. It's not the same as respiration. Once again, there's a
diagram that you have to be able to label. You need to know _how_ the air
gets in. — remember, it's to do with _pressure_ inside and outside, _not_ sucking. Remember what the
alveoli do — their size, number and structure help them to do it. In the Exam, you can be asked to
label diagrams of _gas exchange_ in the _lungs_ and at the _cells_, so don't forget _which way_ the gases go.

Respiration

Understanding Respiration

1) What is the *correct function* of respiration, is it to get air in and out of the lungs, or is to release energy from cells? Do *plants* respire?

2) a) *Copy and complete* the word equation for aerobic respiration.

glucose + _____ → _____ + water (+ energy transferred)

b) The chemical symbol for *glucose* is $C_6H_{12}O_6$. *Copy and complete* the symbol equation for aerobic respiration.

_____ + $6O_2$ → _____CO_2 + $6H_2O$ (+ energy transferred)

c) What substances are *needed* for respiration? How does each substance travel to where it is used in the body. Where do these substances come from?

d) What substances are *produced* by respiration? How do these substances leave the body?

e) *What else* is produced by respiration?

Energy from Glucose

3) Enough energy is released from burning 1g of glucose to power a 100W light bulb for over 2½ minutes!

a) Some of the energy produced by respiration can be used to maintain a steady body temperature in cold surroundings. Give some other uses for this energy in the body.

b) Enzymes are used in respiration to *release energy* in small quantities from the glucose. What would happen if *all the energy* was released into cells at once?

c) The enzymes needed for respiration are contained in an organelle in the cytoplasm of a cell, called a mitochondrion. What do we call *more than one* mitochondrion?

d) The diagram on the right represents a section of a mitochondrion greatly magnified. *Suggest how* the structure of the mitochondrion allows it to carry out the chemical reactions needed for aerobic respiration efficiently.

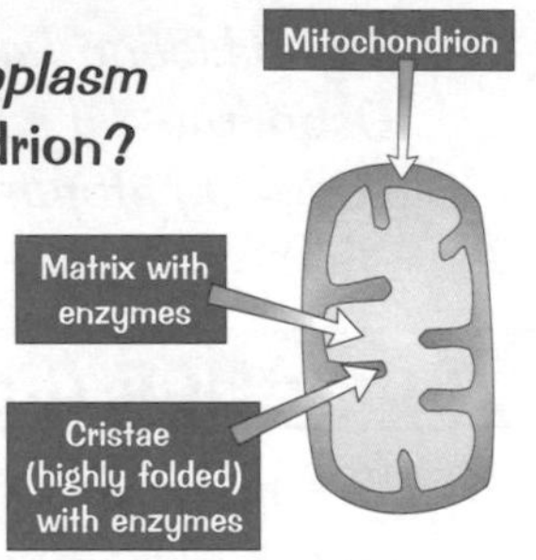

Mitochondrion

Matrix with enzymes

Cristae (highly folded) with enzymes

Energy Transfer

4) Use your correct answers to questions 2) and 3) to help you answer the following:

a) In what forms is *energy* transferred to the surroundings during burning?

b) What are the similarities between *burning* and *respiration*?

c) What are the *differences* between burning and respiration?

5) How could you tell that a *cell* was respiring? You should *aim* for at least *three* answers.

An Experiment using Cobalt Chloride Paper

6) Paul knew that water vapour is produced by respiration, and that leaves respire. He also knew that blue cobalt chloride paper turns pink in the presence of water vapour, so he set up the experiment shown on the right. He only expected to detect water vapour in the boiling tube containing the living leaf. To his surprise, however, the cobalt chloride paper eventually turned pink in both boiling tubes. *Explain* why this happened.

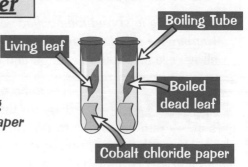

Boiling Tube

Living leaf

Boiled dead leaf

Cobalt chloride paper

Respiration

Animal Respiration

7) Houdini the school hamster certainly eats a lot, but is he respiring? The diagram on the right shows an experiment to see if Houdini is respiring.

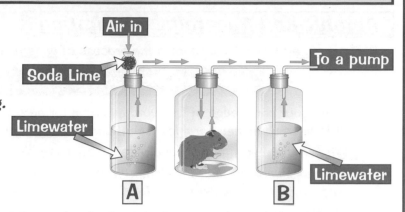

a) If Houdini really is respiring, *which* gases should he produce?

b) Which of these gases will *limewater* detect? What would you see if this gas were present?

c) Soda lime reacts with carbon dioxide. *Why* is it in the funnel where Houdini's air is going in?

d) What do you *expect* to happen to the limewater in flask A? *Explain* your answer.

e) What is the reason for including flask A in the experiment?

f) Explain what *should happen* to the contents of flask B if Houdini really is respiring.

g) After a while, some droplets of condensed water vapour appear on the inside of the middle flask. Suggest some *possible reasons* for this.

Plant Respiration

8) The diagram on the right demonstrates respiration by germinating seeds. Tube A contains soaked, germinating seeds. Tube B contains boiled, dead seeds. Both tubes have some soda lime at the bottom of them. The experiment was set up first thing in the morning, when the beads of oil in the capillary tubes were as shown at X. The experiment was checked again in the afternoon, when the oil in tube A had moved to position Y.

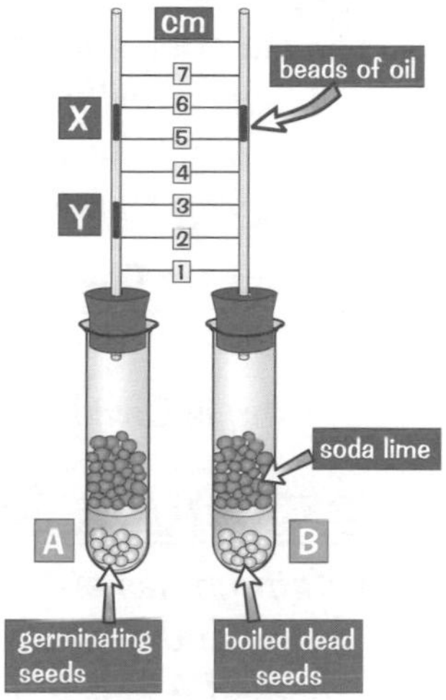

a) *Work out* how far the bead of oil in the capillary tube attached to tube A travelled during the day.

b) What *gas* does soda lime absorb?

c) *Suggest why* the bead of oil in tube B did not move during the day.

d) *Which gas* involved in respiration is the experiment set up to investigate?

e) *Why* does the bead of oil in the capillary tube attached to tube A *move*?

f) What is the *reason* for having tube B as well as tube A?

Metabolic Rate

9) It is possible to measure the rate of oxygen uptake by different animals. A sample of the sort of results obtained is given in the table below.

Animal	Uptake of Oxygen (cm³ of O₂ / kg / min)
Cat	10.5
Dog	5.2
Elephant	1.0
Horse	1.6
Human	3.3
Mouse	26.0
Rat	13.8

a) The rate of oxygen uptake is a measure of the metabolic rate of the organism. What does *metabolic rate* mean?

b) *Copy* the table, putting the animals in order of *increasing* body mass.

c) Plot a *bar chart* to show the rates of oxygen uptake of the different animals. Remember to label your chart *clearly*.

d) *Describe* what your graph shows you about the metabolic rates of different animals. Try to *explain* your findings.

Top Tips: Respiration isn't the same as breathing. Remember this: *Respiration* is the process of converting *Food* to *Energy*. You really have to know the *word* and *symbol* equations for aerobic respiration. It's useful to know the experiments on these pages — these are the sort of questions you're likely to get in the Exam.

Anaerobic Respiration

Aerobic and Anaerobic Respiration

1) The _word equation_ below shows the process of _anaerobic_ respiration in animal cells.

> glucose → lactic acid (+ energy released)

a) Using your knowledge of the word equation for _aerobic_ respiration, describe the similarities and differences between _aerobic_ respiration and _anaerobic_ respiration.

b) _Why_ are the two types of respiration named aerobic and anaerobic?

c) It is possible to measure the amount of energy released by the two processes. Aerobic respiration releases 16kJ from 1g of glucose, and anaerobic respiration releases 833J from 1g of glucose. Which process releases the _most energy_ from glucose? _How many times_ more energy does this process release?

d) Adenosine triphosphate, or ATP, is a chemical made by cells using energy from respiration. ATP acts as a temporary store of energy that can be used to drive the chemical reactions in cells. One molecule of glucose produces 38 molecules of ATP by aerobic respiration, but only 2 molecules of ATP by anaerobic respiration. Suggest a _reason_ for this difference.

An Endurance Test

2) David does a simple experiment to investigate respiration and muscle activity. He rapidly clenches and unclenches his fist, counting how many times he can do this before his hand feels like it's going to fall off. His results are shown in the table on the right.

Number of clenches	
hand lowered	hand raised
68	19

a) Why are David's muscles unable to keep on _contracting_? What chemical causes the pain he feels?

b) Why is David able to keep his muscles working much _longer_ with his hand lowered?

Respiration Rates during Exercise

3) Kathryn has entered a running race. The graph on the right shows the amount of lactic acid in her blood and her rate of oxygen uptake during the race. The race takes place between the times marked A and B on the graph.

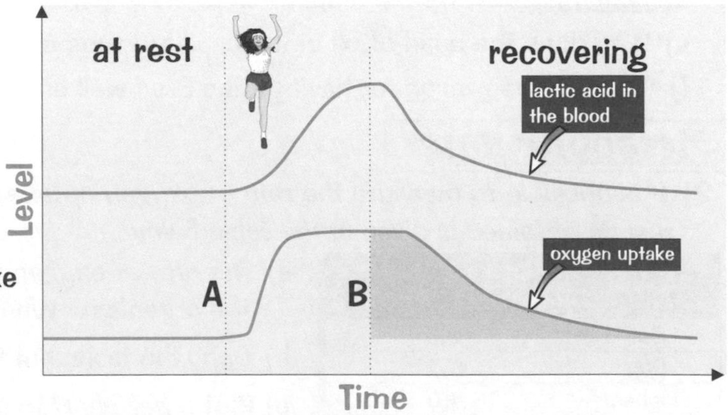

a) What _type_ of respiration is most likely to be occurring when Kathryn is resting before the race?

b) Why does her _rate of oxygen_ uptake increase when she begins to run?

c) Why does Kathryn's rate of oxygen uptake reach a _maximum_ during the race? _Why_ can't she take up any more oxygen than this?

d) Why does the concentration of _lactic acid_ in her blood increase during the race?

e) Why do the concentration of lactic acid in Kathryn's blood and her rate of oxygen uptake take time to return to the resting levels _after_ the race?

f) The _shaded area_ on the graph is known as the _oxygen debt_. What does this mean?

Animal Respiration

4) Some organisms use fermentation as a way of releasing energy from glucose. Animals do not. Suggest a reason _why not_.

Anaerobic Respiration

Fermentation of Glucose

5) Fermentation is a very important process for the bread and alcohol industry.

a) *Copy* and *complete* the following sentences about fermentation choosing the *correct words* from the *underlined pairs*.

> Fermentation is an example of *aerobic* / *anaerobic* respiration. Yeast is a microscopic *bacterium* / *fungus* that can produce *oxygen* / *carbon dioxide* and *water* / *ethanol* from glucose by fermentation.

b) Write down the word *equation* for the fermentation of glucose.

Fermentation using Yeast

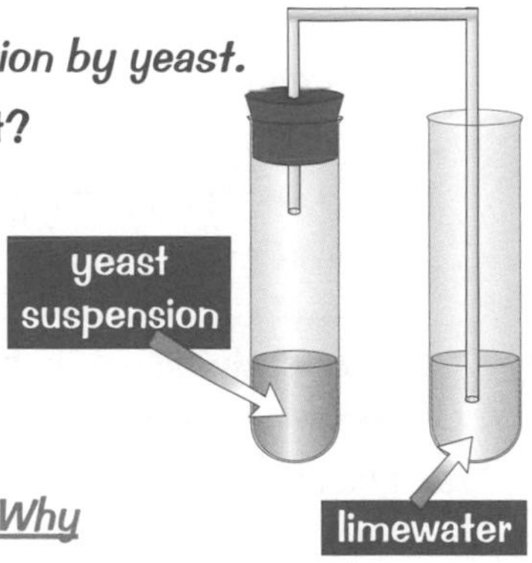

6) *The diagram on the right shows an experiment to demonstrate fermentation by yeast.*

a) What should be *added* to the yeast suspension to let fermentation start?

b) At the start, *oxygen* is present in the air. What *type* of respiration will the yeast use? What is the *advantage* of this for the yeast?

c) Later, the yeast begin to respire differently. What *type* of respiration are they using now? Why does this *change* happen?

d) Explain what *changes* you expect to see in the limewater.

e) After a while the yeast die and sink to the bottom of the boiling tube. *Why* does this happen? *Aim* for *two* answers to this question.

f) *Home wine-makers use an airlock like the one shown opposite. Bubbles of gas can escape out of the "demijohn" (the flask in which the grape juice is being fermented) but air cannot get back in. Suggest why wine-makers use airlocks.*

yeast suspension

limewater

Enzymes and Fermentation

7) The word enzyme means *"in yeast"*. *Suggest why* enzymes have been named in this way.

8) *The carbon dioxide produced by fermentation can be stored under pressure in gas cylinders. This gas can provide the "fizz" in fizzy drinks.* What *other uses* can we make of fermentation?

Releasing Energy

9) The table below summarises the *three main processes* for the releasing of energy from glucose.

a) Complete the table, *choosing* from the following list:

Glucose, Oxygen, Lactic Acid, 0.83, Carbon Dioxide, 1.16, Ethanol, Water, 16

Process	aerobic respiration	anaerobic respiration	fermentation
Reactants			
Products			
Energy released (kJ/g glucose)			

b) Write a short paragraph *comparing* the *two types* of anaerobic respiration you have studied.

Top Tips:
Don't get confused between the words *aerobic* and *anaerobic*. Anaerobic respiration is what happens when there isn't any oxygen around. It gets energy out of glucose, but *not very much*. You need to be able to explain clearly why *hard* exercise *hurts* and why we *carry on panting* afterwards. Remember that *yeast* has a different kind of anaerobic respiration to us — we call it *fermentation* and it makes beer and bread, so hurrah for yeast.

The Nervous System

The Five Sense Organs

1) One of the functions of the nervous system is to allow us to react to changes in our surroundings.

  a) What do we call the _changes_ in the environment to which we respond?

  b) What do we call the _cells_ that detect these changes in the environment?

  c) Suggest some advantages of being able to _detect_ and _respond_ to changes in the environment?

2) You need to know about _five sense organs_, the nose, the tongue, the ears, the eyes and the skin.

  a) _Match_ these sense organs to the following senses (some organs have more than one sense):

balance	hearing	sight	smell	taste	temperature	touch

  b) The senses work because each sense organ contains cells that are able to detect certain stimuli. For example, the sense of balance arises from the appropriate sense organ being able to detect the position of the body. _Match_ the senses in part a) to the following stimuli (some stimuli may produce more than one sense):

chemicals	light	position	sound	pressure	temperature change

  c) _Draw up a table_ with the headings shown on the right. Put your answers to parts a) and b) together to complete your table. It should show _which stimuli_ are detected in each sense organ, and the _sense_ produced as a result.

Sense organ	Stimulus	Sense

Nerve Impulses

3) The receptor cells in sense organs are able to convert or transduce the energy from a stimulus into a nerve impulse. What is a _nerve impulse_? _How many directions_ can a nerve impulse travel in?

Reflexes

4) If you touch a hot object with your finger, you quickly move your finger away without having to think about it. This is a reflex action.

  a) What is the _stimulus_ in this reflex action?

  b) What is the _response_ in this reflex action?

  c) What is the _effector_ that _causes_ this response?

The diagram on the right represents a _reflex arc_.

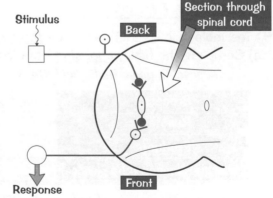

  d) _Copy_ the diagram. _Label_ the sensory neurone, the connector (relay) neurone, and the motor neurone. _Label_ the receptor and the effector in the appropriate circle or box. _Add arrows_ to show the direction of the nerve impulses.

  e) What is the role of the _neurones_ in this reflex action?

  f) Use your answers to _rearrange_ these features of a reflex arc into the correct order:

neurones (coordinator) → effector → receptor → response → stimulus

  g) Use the reflex arc to explain why reflex actions are such _fast responses_.

5) _Describe_ the reflex arcs that are undergone when you are hit just below the knee-cap, and when you get a speck of grit in your eye.

The Nervous System

Neurones

6) The two diagrams on the right show a _sensory neurone_ and a _motor neurone_.
   a) Describe what a _sensory_ neurone and a _motor_ neurone do?
   b) Which diagram, A or B, represents a sensory neurone? _Explain_ how you know this.
   c) _Copy_ the diagrams. Add an _arrow_ to each to show the _direction_ of the nerve impulse. _Label_ as many features as you can in each diagram.
   d) Each neurone is making connections with other nerves or tissues at the part marked X. _Label_ each diagram to show what X is connected to.
   e) _Explain_ how the _structures_ of neurones are adapted to their function.

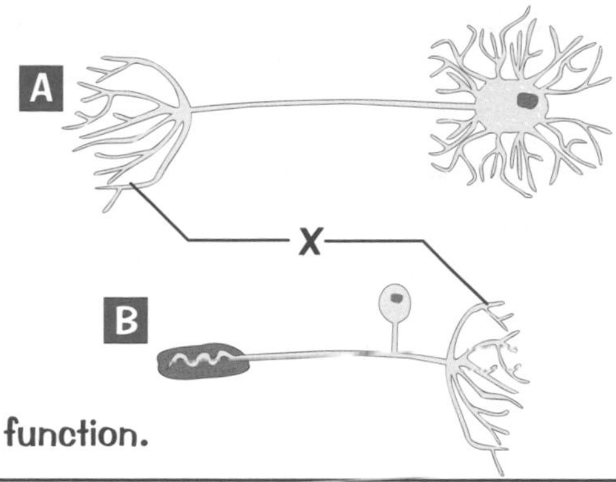

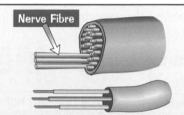

A

B

X

7) _The diagrams on the right show sections through a nerve and an electricity cable._

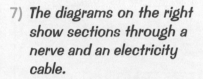

Nerve Fibre

Describe the similarities and differences between a nerve and its nerve fibres (part of a neurone), and the cable.

Reflex Actions

8) _Copy_ these sentences about reflex actions, choosing the correct words from each underlined pair:

"A reflex action is an _conscious_ / _automatic_ response to a _stimulus_ / _receptor_. It happens very _quickly_ / _slowly_ and _involves_ / _does not involve_ the _brian_ / _brain_. Reflex actions allow us to co-ordinate body activity by _remote control_ / _nervous control_."

The Nervous System

9) _Look at the diagram on the right:_
   a) _Identify_ the parts of the nervous system labelled X, Y and Z.
   b) What is the _collective name_ given to the parts represented by X and Y.?
   c) In which _direction_ can nerve impulses travel in the part labelled Y?
   d) Give _two_ functions of the part labelled X. Is X involved in reflex actions?

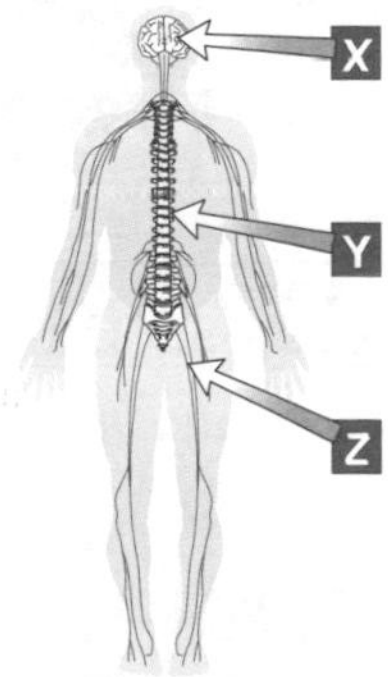

X

Y

Z

Synapses

10) The diagram on the right shows a _synapse_ greatly magnified.
   a) _Where_ do you find synapses? What is the _function_ of a synapse?
   b) What do the _bubbles of chemical_ crossing the synapse do?
   c) There are _mitochondria_ in the diagram. What does this suggest about the working of a synapse?
   d) _Electrical wires can be joined together using solder, a junction box, or simply by twisting the ends together._
      Suggest a reason why neurones _cannot_ be connected together directly in this way.

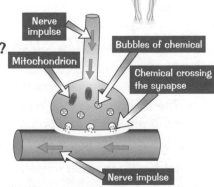

Nerve impulse

Bubbles of chemical

Mitochondrion

Chemical crossing the synapse

Nerve impulse

Top Tips: First, you have to be able to recognise the parts of the nervous system and say what they do. Remember that the whole point about a _reflex_ is that it allows a _rapid response_ to a stimulus _without_ involving the brain. The brain comes in _later_ to allow us to feel the pain. Remember, it's not the pain that goes up the spinal cord, it's the nerve impulse. And don't forget that _chemicals_ bridge the gap between one neurone and another in a _synapse_.

SECTION THREE — HUMAN BIOLOGY PART ONE

The Eye

Identifying the Parts of the Eye

1) Look at the diagram on the right. It shows a _section_ through an eye.

a) _Match_ the names below to the parts of the eye labelled A — H.
Make a _table_ for your answers.

ciliary muscles ☐   cornea ☐   pupil ☐

iris ☐   retina ☐   lens ☐

optic nerve ☐   suspensory ligaments ☐

b) You may also be asked to _identify_ the sclera, the blind spot
and the fovea. _Match_ these parts to the labels X, Y and Z, and add these to your table.

2) Make sure you know what all the parts of the eye do, by matching the _part_ to its _function_:

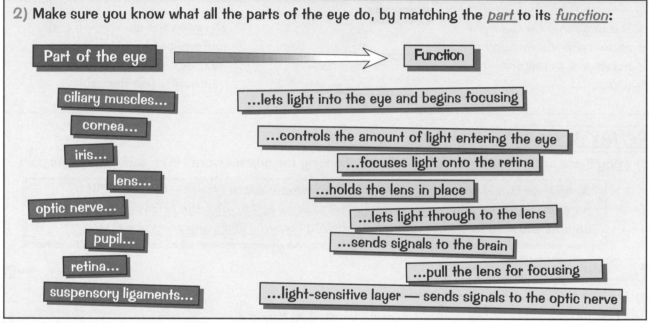

Part of the eye ⟶ Function

ciliary muscles...   ...lets light into the eye and begins focusing

cornea...   ...controls the amount of light entering the eye

iris...   ...focuses light onto the retina

lens...   ...holds the lens in place

optic nerve...   ...lets light through to the lens

pupil...   ...sends signals to the brain

retina...   ...pull the lens for focusing

suspensory ligaments...   ...light-sensitive layer — sends signals to the optic nerve

Transmission of Light in the Eye

3) When light enters the eye, it travels through some parts of the eye but not others.

a) Which _parts_ of the eye does light travel through? Write them down _in order_.

b) Which parts of the eye does light _hit_, but _cannot_ travel through?

The Muscles in the Eye

4) The iris contains circular and radial muscles.
These muscles control the diameter of the pupil.
The diagrams on the right show the iris in two
different light conditions.

a) What is the _black circle_ in the centre?

b) _Identify_ the two muscle types, A and B.

c) Which diagram, 1 or 2, shows the eye in _bright_ light? _Explain_ why you chose this diagram.

d) In diagram 1, which type of muscle is _relaxed_ and which is _contracted_?

e) In diagram 2, which type of muscle is _relaxed_ and which has _contracted_?

f) Use your answers so far to _explain_ how the iris controls the amount of light entering the eye.

g) What _other muscles_ are involved with the eye. What is their _function_?

The Eye

Focusing on Objects

5) The diagrams below show rays of light coming from an object on the left and going through a _thick_ and a _thin_ lens.

thick lens   thin lens

distance = x   distance = x

If a screen were placed where the rays come together on the right of the lens, an image of the object would be seen on the screen — the light from the image would be focused onto the screen.

a) What sort of lens is needed to focus the light from a _distant_ object and from a _nearby_ object?

b) From which diagram are the light rays _bent most_ to come together on the right?

The Lens

6) _For light to be focused onto the retina, it must change direction in the eye._

a) Which _parts_ of the eye can do this?

b) _The lens of our eye is different from the lens of a magnifying glass — it can change its shape from fat to thin._ What is the _advantage_ of doing this?

7) _The diagram on the right shows the lens of the eye focusing a nearby object onto the retina._

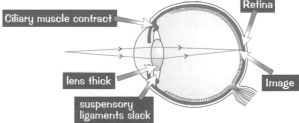

Ciliary muscle contract   Retina

lens thick   Image

suspensory ligaments slack

a) Why must the lens be _thick_ here?

b) The suspensory ligaments are slack. What does that tell you about the _natural shape_ of the lens?

c) _The ciliary muscles in the diagram are in a ring around the lens._ If the ciliary muscles _relax_, what will happen to the _suspensory ligaments_? What will happen to the _lens_?

d) If the lens changes as in part **c**), what sort of object will be _focused_ onto the retina?

e) Draw a _diagram_, similar to the one in this question, to show how light from a distant object can be focused onto the retina. Make sure you _label_ your diagram clearly.

Retina Receptor Cells

8) _The retina contains receptor cells._

a) _What stimulus_ are these cells sensitive to?

b) What happens when the _receptor cells_ in the retina are stimulated?

c) What is the function of the _optic nerve_?

9) _There are two types of receptor in the retina, named after their shapes. The table below gives information about them, but some of it is muddled up._
Write down the information _correctly_.

	RODS	CONES
Number in retina	about 120 million	about 6 million
Found in	mainly the fovea, few elsewhere	all the retina, but few in fovea
Sensitive to colour	yes	no
Work in dim light	yes	no

Top Tips:
As ever, you need to _learn the diagram_ of the eye and be able to label _all_ the different parts. Remember the differences between _rods_ and _cones_. You've got to understand _how_ the eye focuses images of near and distant objects on the retina. Remember how the _iris_ makes the pupil get bigger and smaller to vary the amount of light getting into the eye.

Hormones

Hormone Processes within the Body

1) _Copy_ and _complete_ the following sentences by adding the most suitable words from the box:

receptors	hormones	systems	glands
nervous system	bloodstream	chemicals	

Many processes within the body are coordinated by _____ called _____ . These substances are produced by _____ and transported to their target organs by the _____ .

Hormones, Glands and their Functions

2) _Copy_ and _complete_ the following table.

Name of hormone	Gland	Function
a) Insulin		turns glucose to glycogen
b)	Pancreas	turns glycogen to glucose
c) Oestrogen		develops female sexual characteristics
d) Follicle Stimulating Hormone (FSH)		causes eggs to mature and ovaries to produce oestrogen
e) LH (Luteinising Hormone)	Pituitary	

Hormone Production

3) The diagram opposite shows the system that controls the body's blood-sugar level.

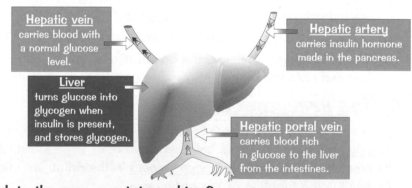

Hepatic vein carries blood with a normal glucose level.

Hepatic artery carries insulin hormone made in the pancreas.

Liver turns glucose into glycogen when insulin is present, and stores glycogen.

Hepatic portal vein carries blood rich in glucose to the liver from the intestines.

a) If a meal _rich in carbohydrate_ was eaten, what substance would be found to excess in the blood?

b) Which _hormone_ would this stimulate the pancreas into making?

This hormone initiates the changing of the excess glucose to form in which it can be stored.

c) Which _organ_ does this and in what form does it store it?

d) Complete the _flow diagram_ opposite to show how the blood-sugar level is returned to normal after a meal rich in carbohydrates.

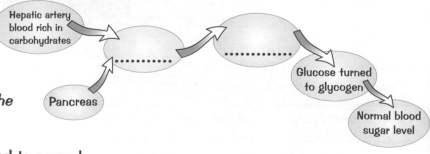

Hepatic artery blood rich in carbohydrates

Pancreas

Glucose turned to glycogen

Normal blood sugar level

e) After a work-out in the gym the blood-sugar level falls below normal. _Explain_ how it would be returned to normal.

The Use of Hormones

Using Hormones to Control Body Functions

4) The *hormones and treatments* below are given by doctors to control various body functions. *Match* each with the correct description.

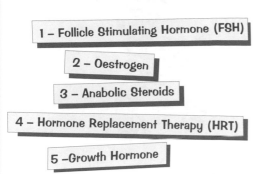

1 – Follicle Stimulating Hormone (FSH)

2 – Oestrogen

3 – Anabolic Steroids

4 – Hormone Replacement Therapy (HRT)

5 –Growth Hormone

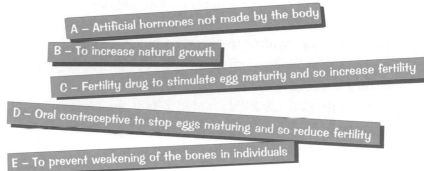

A – Artificial hormones not made by the body

B – To increase natural growth

C – Fertility drug to stimulate egg maturity and so increase fertility

D – Oral contraceptive to stop eggs maturing and so reduce fertility

E – To prevent weakening of the bones in individuals

The many Types and Functions of Hormones

5) *Write* a sentence to explain each of the following terms:

> hormone, glands, insulin, glucagon, anabolic steroid, FSH, oestrogen, HRT.

6) *Explain* in a sentence the *meaning* or *function* of each of the following terms:

> glucose, glycogen, pancreas, liver, ovaries, pituitary.

Hormones Travel from Glands to Organs

7) *The bloodstream provides the method of transport that enables hormones to reach their target organ.*

a) Using the labels below, *copy and complete* the diagram opposite showing the production and action of hormones in the body.

endocrine gland   response

target organ   bloodstream

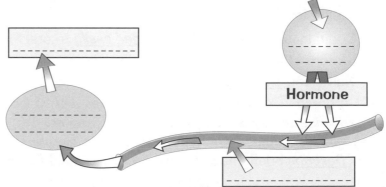

Stimulus

Hormone

b) *There are* <u>two</u> *types of messenger in the body —* <u>chemical</u> *ones (hormones) and* <u>nervous</u> *ones.* Name <u>four</u> differences between the two types. (Think about the speed of the message and the way they act).

Top Tips: Don't forget that any hormone released into the blood will go to <u>all</u> organs — but it's only the *target organs* that'll respond to it. You might get an Exam question that compares the *endocrine system* with, say, the *nervous system* — so think about ways they're different — and also how they *work together*. Most importantly though, you must know the hormones in Question 2 — for each you should know the *when*, *where* and *why* of its *production* and *effects*.

Insulin Diabetes

The Pancreas and Diabetes

1) *The diagram opposite shows a number of bodily organs in magenta, with glands coloured black.* <u>Label</u> the pancreas on a copy of the diagram.

2) a) Name the two <u>hormones</u> produced by the pancreas that control the level of blood-sugar.
   b) How is production of one of these hormones different in someone with diabetes?
   c) How do you think this would affect the levels of <u>glucose</u> in the bloodstream?

3) State <u>two</u> ways in which a diabetic person might cope with this problem.

4) Name a problem a diabetic person could face when:
   i) the blood-sugar level becomes <u>too low</u>.
   ii) the blood-sugar level becomes <u>too high</u>.

5) How much <u>glycogen</u> would you expect there to be in the liver of a diabetic person? <u>Explain</u> your answer.

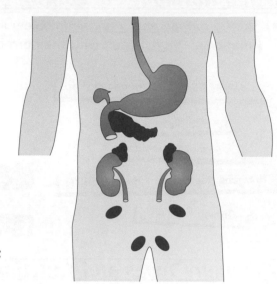

How Insulin helps Diabetics

6) *The work of the hormone insulin is an example of a* <u>negative feedback mechanism</u> *because the release of insulin tends to result in a situation where less insulin is required.*
   a) Explain how the blood-glucose level in a non-diabetic is <u>lowered</u> if it is <u>too high</u>.
   b) Explain how the blood-glucose level in a non-diabetic is <u>increased</u> if it is <u>too low</u>.

7) *Glucagon secretion is a response controlled by the blood-sugar level.*
   a) Give an example of when the blood-sugar level could be <u>rapidly reduced</u>.
   b) In this case, what would happen to <u>glucagon</u> production and how would this return blood-sugar level back to normal?

8) Could insulin injections be <u>changed easily</u> to oral medicine and so make it more attractive to diabetics? <u>Explain</u> your answer.

9) Name any <u>enzymes</u> that could digest insulin.

10) *A person was thought to have diabetes and so was asked by the doctor to produce a sample of urine to test at the pathology laboratories.*
    a) What <u>substance</u> would be tested for in the urine?
    b) <u>Describe</u> briefly how you would test a liquid for the presence of this substance.

Understanding the Terminology

11) <u>Unscramble</u> the following key words linked with this section. There is a clue to help you.

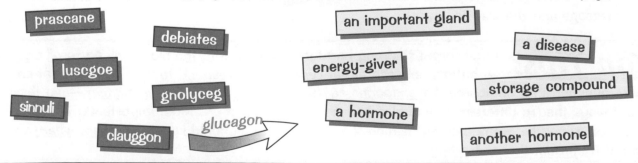

prascane

debiates

an important gland

a disease

luscgoe

energy-giver

storage compound

sinnuli

gnolyceg

a hormone

clauggon → glucagon

another hormone

<u>*Insulin Diabetes*</u>

<u>*Blood-sugar Levels*</u>

12) *In the normal healthy adult the liver contains 100g glycogen and has a blood-sugar level of between 80-100mg/100cm³.*

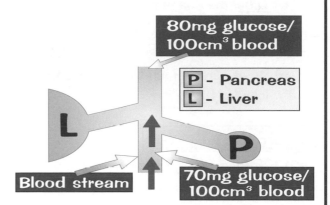

80mg glucose/ 100cm³ blood

P - Pancreas
L - Liver

L

P

Blood stream

70mg glucose/ 100cm³ blood

a) <u>*Copy*</u> the diagram opposite. Draw <u>*labelled lines*</u> showing the directions in which glucagon and glucose would move if the blood-sugar level <u>*fell below*</u> 70mg/100cm³ in the blood.

b) What would happen if the person was diabetic, and their blood-sugar level fell to 40mg/100cm³?

<u>*Blood-Sugar and Insulin levels*</u>

13) *The graph opposite shows blood-sugar and insulin levels of a non-diabetic person taking three meals a day.*

Key
— = glucose
- - = insulin

Breakfast   Dinner   Tea

The graph opposite shows blood-sugar and insulin levels of a diabetic person having three meals and three injections of insulin a day.

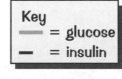

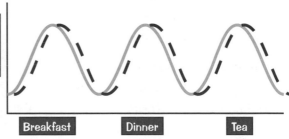

Key
— = glucose
- - = insulin

Breakfast   Dinner   Tea

a) What do you notice about the <u>*shape*</u> of the blood-sugar and insulin graphs of the <u>*non-diabetic*</u> person?

b) If the diabetic person has <u>*three*</u> injections of insulin per day what would you notice about their blood-sugar and insulin levels compared to a non-diabetic person?

c) <u>*Draw a graph*</u> to show what would happen if the diabetic forgot to take an insulin injection at tea time. <u>*Explain the shape of your graph*</u>.

Top Tips:
This insulin stuff shouldn't cause any major problems — as long as you know how it <u>*all fits together*</u>. Remember that insulin acts on the <u>*liver*</u>, and <u>*not*</u> on the blood sugar itself — that's very important. Make sure you can draw a <u>*flow diagram*</u> showing the body's response to too much or too little blood-sugar — then you'll know if you <u>*really*</u> understand it. Any question on insulin is bound to ask about <u>*diabetes*</u> — so you've simply got to know how diabetics can <u>*control*</u> their <u>*blood-sugar*</u> levels — don't forget less obvious things like <u>*exercise*</u>.

The Menstrual Cycle

The Female Reproductive System

1) The diagram opposite shows parts of the female reproductive system.

   a) *Label* the diagram.

   b) What *substance* does the shaded area labelled c) consist of?

   c) What can be found in the structure labelled b)?

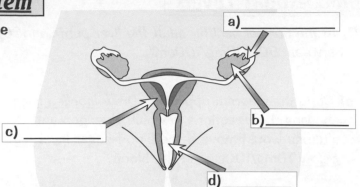

a)_____

b)_____

c) _____

d)_____

A 28-Day Cycle

2) If fertilisation *has not* taken place, the lining of the uterus breaks down. What is the name given to this process?

3) What name is given to the *release* of an egg from the ovary?

4) *The female reproductive cycle can be seen as the journey undertaken by the egg and its development during that time.*

   a) What is the *process* of preparation, egg release and breakdown in the uterus of a woman called?

   b) In what *two* ways could the process continue after ovulation?

5) *How many* eggs are generally released every month?

Preparation, Egg Release and Breakdown

6) Fill in the gaps in the sentences below to describe what happens to the uterus during the menstrual cycle.

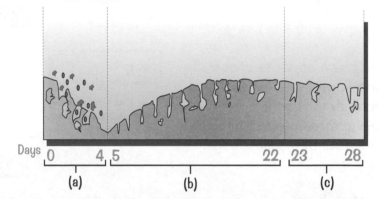

Days 0   4 5   22 23   28

   (a)   (b)   (c)

   a) Levels of the hormone _____ fall and this causes the lining of the uterus to _____ . This is known as _____ .

   b) Levels of the hormone _____ increase, and this causes the lining of the uterus to _____ with _____ _____ ready to receive a _____ ____ .

   c) An increase in the production of _____ maintains the _____ _____ until around day ____ . If no _____ ____ has landed there by then, the spongy lining begins to break down and the cycle begins again.

Egg Release

7) Do both ovaries contain *immature eggs*?

8) Approximately how long into the menstrual cycle is the mature egg *released* from the ovary?

9) *Why* are there only a few days in each menstrual cycle when fertilisation is likely to occur?

10) *A healthy woman produces approximately 400-500 eggs in her lifetime.* Are all of the eggs *mature*? If not, *when* do they become mature?

The Menstrual Cycle

Ovulation

11) What is the _period of time_ between successive ovulations called?

12) What happens to the _uterus_ between each ovulation?

13) How many _eggs_ are likely to be fertilised at once?

14) _The diagram opposite shows what happens in the ovary during the menstrual cycle._
a) What is occurring at B?
b) What _hormone_ is produced during period C?
c) At D, this hormone is no longer produced. What do we call the _period_ which follows this?

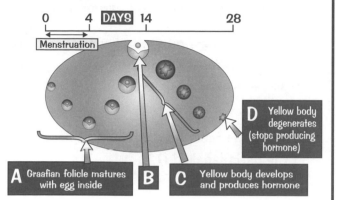

15) _Explain_ the meaning of the following terms: —

> ova,   ovary,   puberty,   ovulation,   Fallopian tube,   uterus,   cervix,   vagina,   menstruation,   menstrual cycle.

Growth of the Reproductive and other Organs

16) _The graph on the right shows the varying growth rates of the reproductive and other organs as we grow up._

Explain the shapes of the curves A, B and C.

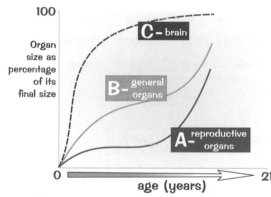

The Menopause

17) What happens to the menstrual cycle during _pregnancy_?

18) Explain what the _menopause_ is and when it happens.

19) The boxes below show some terms associated with the female reproductive cycle, together with explanations. _Match_ the correct explanation A - F with the terms 1 - 6.

1) Ovary
2) Uterus
3) Menstruation
4) Fallopian Tube/ Oviduct
5) Ovum
6) Pregnancy

A) The tube which leads from the ovaries to the uterus
B) The events which occur after fertilisation of an egg
C) An egg that the female produces
D) The female organ which produces eggs
E) The monthly breakdown of the uterine lining
F) The main female organ which houses the developing foetus

Top Tips: Lots more interacting hormones and glands to learn. But if you can draw and label a _diagram_ with all the bits of the female _reproductive system_, and if you can say _what's happening_ at all the _stages_ of the _menstrual cycle_ — then you'll have pretty much got it. Just make sure you know what all the parts actually _do_.

Hormones in the Menstrual Cycle

Hormone Sites in the Body

1) What type of *tissue* produces hormones?
2) Which *part* of the body carries these hormones?

3) In total, *four* hormones control menstruation. Name the *two* places where they are produced.

4) *Copy* the table opposite and fill in the parts labelled i) to iv).

Hormone Name	Source	Function
FSH (Follicle Stimulating Hormone)	Pituitary	i)
Oestrogen	Ovaries	ii)
iii)	Pituitary	Stimulates the release of an egg
Progesterone	iv)	Causes uterus lining to become thicker and full of blood vessels

Hormones Controlling the Menstrual Cycle

5) The diagram opposite shows the order in which the glands and hormones are involved in the menstrual cycle.

a) Fill in the missing *hormones* (i), (ii) and (iii).

b) What is the name of the *gland* which produces hormones (i) and (iii)?

c) Which other hormone is produced by the ovaries to *maintain* the lining of the uterus?

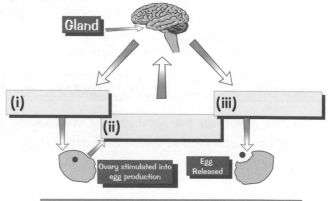

Non-Fertilisation

6) *Copy* and *complete* the diagram below to show what happens at different stages of the menstrual cycle and during pregnancy.

7) With the help of the diagram, answer the following questions:

a) Name the *hormone* that brings about the *repair and thickening* of the uterus lining.

b) Name the *hormone* that *maintains* the uterus lining and prepares the body for pregnancy.

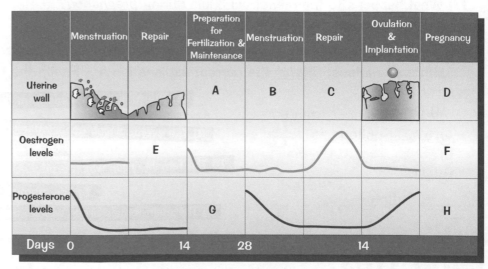

8) What do you understand by a *"target organ"* in the menstrual cycle?

Hormones in the Menstrual Cycle

The Role of Hormones

9) _Copy_ and _complete_ the diagram, filling in the unknown hormones 1 & 2, and the missing effects A & B.

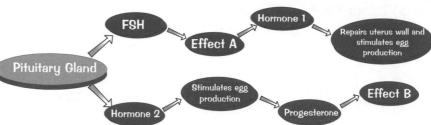

The Pill

10) _"The Pill" is a contraceptive taken by women that works by controlling egg production._
   a) Which _two_ hormones does the pill contain?
   b) What do you think the effect of taking the pill _regularly_ would be on the level of oestrogen in the body?
   Maintaining oestrogen at this level inhibits production of FSH.
   c) After a period of time, what effect would this have on _egg production_?
   d) Would you expect the egg production of someone on the pill to _return to normal_ after they stopped taking it? Why?

11) Are the effects of taking the pill an example of a _feedback mechanism_? Explain your answer.

Fertility, Pregnancy and Feedback Control

12) _Women's fertility can be altered with the introduction of a particular hormone._
   a) Which hormone would be given to _increase_ the fertility of a woman?
   b) _Explain_ how this hormone has the required effect.

13) _The period of pregnancy also stimulates the production of a particular hormone._
   a) Which hormone _remains_ in production throughout pregnancy?
   b) _Explain_ why this needs to happen

14) Using the normal menstrual cycle as an example, state _two ways_ in which one hormone has a _"feedback control"_ on another hormone.

Controlling Fertility in Women

15) _Fertility treatment can be used by couples who are having problems conceiving. Part of this treatment can involve stimulating egg production._
   a) Which hormone would be taken to stimulate _egg development_?
   b) Which hormone is then produced by the ovaries to stimulate _egg release_?
   c) Give _two_ examples of problems with this treatment.

Top Tips:
All these hormones can be pretty tricky — especially the way they _interact_ with each other. But you've really got to know it — for _each hormone_, you must know _what controls it_ and _what it controls_. I'd say drawing a _graph_ of all the hormone levels should fix the details in that brain of yours — and it's this sort of graph that tends to appear in the Exams. Finally, don't forget which hormones are used in _oral contraceptives_ and _fertility drugs_.

66

Disease in Humans

Identifying Microbes

1) a) Name the _two_ different types of microbe.
   b) In what _conditions_ do most everyday microbes tend to live and multiply well?
   c) What _effects_ can microbes have in our bodies?

2) Name the _two different_ types of microbes shown opposite.

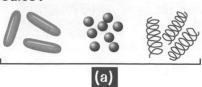
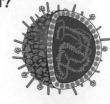

(a)

(b)

The Key Features of Microbes

3) _Copy_ and _complete_ the following table below by deciding whether each property in the box applies to bacteria, viruses or both.

about 1/10,000mm, about 1/100,000mm, can produce toxins, cell wall, slime capsule, always contain DNA, coat of protein, cytoplasm, can reproduce rapidly.

	Bacteria	Viruses
1		
2		
3		
4		
5		
6		
7		
8		

Bacteria in the Body

4) _Bacteria are extremely tiny (about 1/100th the size of most body cells), which enables them to enter the human body very easily._

   a) What process of _gaseous exchange_ does their small size allow bacteria to use?

   b) Name the substance used to _kill_ bacteria in swimming pools.

5) Name two situations that allow _large numbers_ of microbes to enter the body.

6) State three conditions in the body that make the it an _ideal place_ for microbes to grow.

Defence Mechanisms

7) What does the word "_pathogen_" mean?

8) What are the _three_ main groups of pathogens?

9) Which one of the main groups of pathogens only _occasionally_ produces a disease?

10) _Copy_ and _complete_ the table below, stating the type of microbe that causes the disease and _how_ the disease then spreads.

Disease	Type of microbe (bacteria, virus, fungus) that causes it	How it is spread (air droplets, infected water, food contamination)
Common cold		
Measles		
Cholera		
Polio		
Whooping cough		

Disease in Humans

Effects on Living Cells

11) Members of which group of pathogens grow inside _living cells_?

12) If we wanted to grow a virus we would need a supply of cells. We use a procedure known as "tissue culture" to grow them.

 a) Explain fully what the term _tissue culture_ means.

 b) Using a sequence of _diagrams_ and _brief explanations_, explain the stages of the development of a virus inside a cell.

 c) What do you think the virus _competes_ with the cell for once inside? _How else_ does the virus affect the cell?

Viruses and How they spread

13) _Explain_ how a cold-sufferer could pass on their cold to another person by sneezing.

14) Name _four ways_ in which microbes can _spread_ and so pass on a disease.

15) a) What type of conditions are _bad_ for bacterial growth?

 b) How do bacteria _protect_ themselves from these types of conditions?

16) _Both viruses and bacteria can develop from just a few into a large colony very quickly. This can be difficult for the body to deal with._

 If the infection was _bacterial_, how might you help your body get rid of the infection? And if it was _viral_?

17) Give _three ways_ in which you could stop microbes developing and spreading in your home.

Vitamin Deficiency Diseases

18) Vitamins are important to many areas and functions of the body. Without them you can develop deficiency diseases. _Copy_ and _complete_ the table opposite showing the _symptoms_ of a deficiency of each vitamin.

Vitamin	Symptoms of Deficiency
A	
B	
C	
D	
K	

Questions on Tuberculosis

19) _Tuberculosis_ (TB) is a deadly bacterial disease that is on the increase in this country.

 a) Which _organs_ will be infected _first_ if the TB bacterium is breathed in?

 b) What _symptoms_ would you see in someone infected with the TB bacterium?

 c) What is the possible link between TB and _unpasteurised milk_?

 d) Why is it _more likely_ that people living in _overcrowded_ areas will catch TB?

 e) How does the _BCG_ vaccination for TB _prevent_ a person catching the disease?

Top Tips: The most important thing here is to know your _bacterium_ and _virus_ inside out — so you'd better be able to _draw_ them (and _label_ the bits). Exam questions will often tell you how _fast_ a bacterium _divides_, and then ask you how many there'll be a day or so later — so make sure you can work this out. Don't forget the things that affect their numbers — like _competition_, _food supply_, _temperature_ and _toxins_. And you might be asked how _lifestyle_ and _living conditions_ can affect the spread of disease — so be warned.

Fighting Disease

The Role played by Blood Cells

1) The body has many natural defence systems to prevent infection and disease. List *three* of these natural defences.

2) *Match* the correct name below to each of the blood cells a)-c).

Phagocyte

Erythrocyte (red blood cell)

Lymphocyte

a) 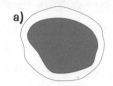 b)   c)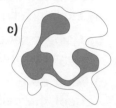

3) Which of these blood cells carries *oxygen* by changing haemoglobin to oxyhaemoglobin?

4) Which of the blood cells produces *antibodies*?

5) If bacteria enter the body, special blood cells respond automatically.
   Which type of blood cell *engulfs* bacteria? *Explain* how the bacteria are then destroyed?

6) The human body is protected by a versatile tough outer layer. This is of course the skin.
   a) What is the *outer* layer of the skin called?
   b) What *features* of this outer layer *prevent* the entry of pathogens?
   c) Under what circumstances do you think a pathogen could enter the body *through the skin*?

Preventing the spread of Infection

7) Clotting is an important defence mechanism of the body.
   a) Which two parts of the blood are involved in *clotting* a wound?
   b) Give *two* reasons why blood clotting is important

8) Use the boxes below to draw a *flow diagram* showing how the body deals with toxins.

toxins

pathogen

destruction of toxins

leucocyte

antitoxins

9) Some people have a natural immunity to a particular microbe — that is they have naturally acquired antibodies to fight it.
   a) How do you think a person might have got this *natural immunity*?

   There are diseases that are serious enough that it is worth trying to prevent them *before* they occur. The first scientist to do this was Edward Jenner.
   b) What is this *process* called? *How* does it work?

10) It is possible to protect against an infection by a vaccination (either injected or given orally).
    a) *What vaccinations* might be given to a person who, for example, cuts their foot badly with a garden spade? Explain *why* it could be necessary to do this.

The Social Impacts of Epidemics

11) *The table below* shows the trend in the annual death rate due to diphtheria in England and Wales between 1910 and 1960.
    a) Draw *a bar chart* of these figures.
    b) *Describe* the trend shown.
    c) *Explain* the trend.

Year	1910	1920	1930	1940	1950	1960
Number of deaths	4920	4875	2706	2721	35	10

12) Tuberculosis (TB) is a disease now increasing in Britain. What would be the most *effective* practical programme to *control* and *reduce* the spread of this disease?

Fighting Disease

Blood Disorders

13) *The two diagrams below show samples of blood taken from a healthy person and a person suffering from a disease. It is possible that the diseased person is anaemic since their blood seems to contain fewer red cells. Alternatively, the excess number of white cells could indicate that they are suffering from leukaemia.*

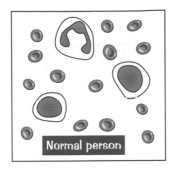

Normal person

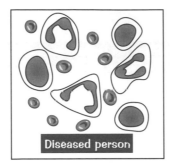

Diseased person

a) How might the abnormal composition of the diseased person's blood *affect* them?

b) *A sample of healthy blood could in fact resemble that of the diseased person in some circumstances. Can you think what such circumstances might be?*

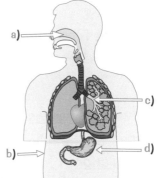

14) Look at the *diagram* to the *right* and *state* how infection is fought in parts (a), (b), (c) and (d).

Infectious Diseases

15) *Infectious diseases kill a lot of people in many developing countries.* Give *four* reasons why infectious diseases are *more prevalent* in these countries.

16) *HIV is a disease which threatens all societies — in both developing and developed countries.*

a) What does *the abbreviation HIV* stand for?

b) What does this *virus* do?

17) *With few exceptions AIDS claims the lives of all that contract it.*

a) What does the abbreviation *AIDS* stand for?

b) How are AIDS and HIV *related*?

c) Give *two ways* in which **HIV** can be *passed on*.

18) Use the list of *infectious diseases* below to *complete* the table (two are not used).

Diphtheria, Whooping cough, Mumps, Tetanus, Measles, Rubella, Polio, Tuberculosis.

MMR Vaccine protects against	DPT Vaccine protects against

Top Tips: Some kind of disease question always seems to find its way into the Exam, so you'd better know this stuff. Learn your *blood cells* — be prepared to *draw* them and say what they do. And apart from the immune system, the body's not short on ways to *keep microbes out* in the first place — make sure you know how the *skin*, *tears*, *breathing organs*, *stomach* and *blood clots* all help do this. And if that fails, there's always *vaccinations* and *antibiotics* — you could well be asked all about them. Nothing too hard here, but don't forget that antibiotics *don't* work on *viruses*.

Drugs

What is Meant by Drugs

1) Drugs are classified as chemicals which can affect human behaviour.
Name *three* of the main groups of drugs.

2) What does it *mean* to say that a drug is:
a) obtained from *living* things?
b) *man-made*?

3) *Copy* and *complete* the table opposite, showing the effects of different types of drugs on the nervous system.

Drug type	Effect on brain and rest of nervous system	Examples of drug type
Sedatives	(a) ---------------------------	Valium / barbiturates
(b) --------------	Speed up the brain and increase alertness	Ecstasy / cocaine milder drug (c) ---------------
(d) -------------	Cause hallucinations	Cannabis, LSD
(e) -------------	Reduce sense of pain	Paracetamol / heroin

4) Give *two reasons* why drugs are dangerous.

5) What do the following words *mean* in relation to drugs?
a) *addiction*
b) *withdrawal*

Solvent Abuse and Painkillers

6) Drugs come in all shapes and forms — not just tablets and pills. This is evident with solvents.
a) What are *solvents*?
b) Why do we often refer to *solvent abuse* as "glue-sniffing"?
c) What are the four *main organs* that glue-sniffing affects?
d) What *symptoms* may a glue-sniffer display?

7) a) Name *two* examples of painkillers.
b) *Heroin is a particularly dangerous form of painkiller because it is very addictive.*
What *problems* can this drug cause?

The Side-effects

8) *Copy* and *complete* the table below for the spaces labelled a) — h).

Drug Group	Highs	Lows	Long-term effects
Stimulants	a)_____	Anxiety, Irritability	b)_____
c)_____	Distorts the senses	d)_____	Causes breathing disorders if smoked
Barbiturates	e)_____	Insomnia, Irritability	f)_____
g)_____	Total relaxation kills pain	Sickness, apathy, self-neglect	h)_____

Drugs

Drugs and their Effects

9) The boxes to the right show a number of *drugs* and their *effects*. Match each drug A-F with the correct effect 1-6.

A) Painkillers
B) Antibiotics
C) Anaesthetics
D) Heroin
E) Tobacco
F) Solvents

1) Prevent pain during an operation
2) Causes severe addiction
3) Reduce pain
4) Causes lung disease and heart disease
5) Kill bacteria
6) Damage brain, liver and kidneys

Organs Affected by Specific Drugs

10) a) *Identify* organs 1) to 5) in the illustration below.

1)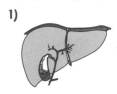
2)
3)
4)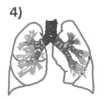
5)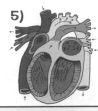

A) Solvent   B) Alcohol   C) Tobacco   D) Stimulants   E) Sedatives

b) For *each* drug A – E in the box above, list which of the *organs* it affects (it might be more than one).

The Consequences of Addiction

11) *If a person is dependent on a drug they are said to be addicted to that drug.*
a) Name the two *different* types of addiction.
b) Give three examples of *physical symptoms* that *withdrawal* from a drug might cause.

12) *Complete* the following sentences on a number of common drugs.

Stimulants affect the _____ system and give a person a feeling of increased energy. _____, found in tea, coffee and some soft drinks, is a m_____ stimulant and fairly harmless, though people will often suffer from h_____ after reducing their intake. On the other hand, stronger stimulants, such as a_____, are very dangerous. Prolonged use can lead to h_____ and p_____ c_____, and coming off them results in severe d_____. Ecstasy (a h_____) in smaller doses has a similar effect and gives a feeling of boundless _____ which can put a person at risk of o_____ and d_____.

Painkillers are another class of drug. The stronger ones such as _____ are hugely addictive. Its expense often means that users turn to _____ as a way of financing their habit, and the severe _____ symptoms make it difficult to give up. It is also easy to o_____.

Solvents are easily available drugs and are contained in such things as p_____ and g_____. Their effects are wide-ranging and include b_____ problems and damage to many vital organs such as the _____, _____, _____ and _____.

Top Tips: Drugs are substances that can alter the way in which the body works. You need to know *how* the four main types of drugs in Question 3 affect the body. Remember that painkillers, tranquillisers and sleeping pills are *helpful* to people who are *ill*, but they are often *abused*. Don't forget that when the body has got *used* to the *effects* of a drug *painful* and *unpleasant withdrawal symptoms* happen when the person tries to stop taking the drug — this is what creates physical *addiction*.

Alcohol

Consuming Alcohol

1) Quite apart from its effect on a person's behaviour, alcohol consumption can severely affect the body's ability to function properly.
   a) What _system_ in the body is most affected by alcohol in the short term?
   b) What are the _short-term_ effects of moderate alcohol consumption?

2) Which two _organs_ in the body are most prone to _damage_ by _long-term_ excessive alcohol consumption?

3) _Look_ at these _two diagrams_, then answer the questions that follow:

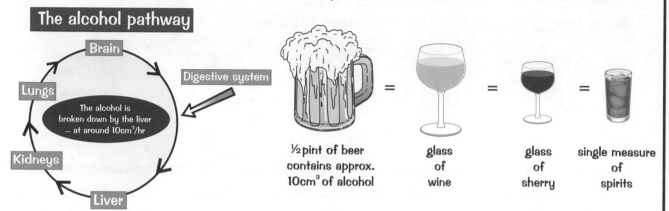

The alcohol pathway

Brain — Digestive system — The alcohol is broken down by the liver — at around 10cm³/hr — Lungs — Kidneys — Liver

½ pint of beer contains approx. 10cm³ of alcohol = glass of wine = glass of sherry = single measure of spirits

   a) _A person at an office party has 2 double whiskies, 3 glasses of wine and a pint of beer. Approximately_ how much _alcohol have they consumed? (Show your working.)_
   b) What is the _earliest_ time that the person in the question above would have their body _free from alcohol_ if they drank from midday to 3pm? (Show your working.)

People who Should Avoid Alcohol

4) Why would it be _dangerous_ to give a person suffering from hypothermia a drink of brandy or whisky?

5) Why is taking a drop of alcohol before competing in a very important sporting event _not_ recommended?

6) _Cirrhosis_ is a disease most commonly caused by _long-term alcoholism_.
   Which _organ_ does this disease affect in alcoholics?

Moderation makes Good Sense

7) What is an _alcoholic_?

8) Why do alcoholics often suffer from _deficiency diseases_?

9) Why is drinking and driving a _stupid_ combination?

10) Give a _reason_ why the same amount of alcohol would be likely to have a greater effect on a small person than on a large person.

11) State _three_ of the _long-term_ effects of _constant heavy drinking_.

12) _Complete_ the following sentences on the uses and effects of alcohol.

> Alcohol is usually used for r_____ or to relieve s_____. It s_____ down the brain and can make you feel less i_____. However, excessive drinking can lead to both l_____ disease and a drop in _____ function. Recovering alcoholics often suffer from d_____ and sickness.

Tobacco

Substances in Tobacco

1) Name the main *addictive substance* found in tobacco.

2) Name two harmful substances that are *produced* when tobacco is burnt.

3) What is the name of the *most serious* lung problem caused by tobacco smoke?

4) Name two other *lung diseases* caused by tobacco smoke.

5) *Carbon monoxide produced by smoking has a serious effect on red blood cells.*
   Explain *why* this gas is so dangerous.

Anti-Social Consequences of Smoking

6) How can smoking affect the *blood vessels*?

7) What is *"smoker's cough"* and how is it caused?

8) What is *"passive smoking"*?

9) State *four* effects of *passive smoking* on a person's health.

10) Why are *pregnant* women who smoke strongly advised to give up?

Lung Disease and Smoking

11) *The diagrams to the right show the alveoli of a normal lung and that of someone suffering from emphysema.*

    Which diagram is which? *Explain* your answer.

12) *Lung cancer is linked with smoking.*
    a) Tar in cigarette smoke affects the cells in the lungs. How could this cause *lung cancer*?
    b) *Why* is painful lung action a common symptom of lung cancer?

13) *Complete* the following sentences on the effects of tobacco.

Nicotine makes up a very small part of tobacco, but it is a_____. Many severe long-term effects of smoking are caused by the tar in tobacco smoke. This c_____ the insides of the _____, preventing the efficient removal of f_____ bodies, including b_____. This can lead to e_____, b_____ and l___c_____. And as if that wasn't enough, it also causes diseases of the h_____ and b_____ v_____, leading to heart attacks and strokes. People trying to stop smoking often suffer headaches, d_____ and problems with their appetite.

Top Tips:
Alcohol and tobacco are both legal in this country, but they can still do a lot of harm to the body. Make sure you understand the effects of alcohol — it damages the liver and brain, and it can be addictive. Alcohol *slows down* reactions big-style, which makes driving while drunk *horribly dangerous*. Remember, in tobacco smoke, *nicotine* is the *addictive* substance, and *tar* damages the lungs. Emphysema, lung cancer, heart disease and strokes are all effects of smoking tobacco. Basically, it's bad for you. Don't forget that *passive smoking* can also damage your health. It's hard to give up smoking because nicotine is *very* addictive, and smokers also have a *psychological dependency*.

Homeostasis

Processes that involve the Whole Body

1) What does the word *homeostasis* mean?

2) What *group* of substances coordinates homeostasis?

3) The body produces two main *waste* substances that it needs to get rid of.
   a) *Name* these two substances.
   b) For each, say which *process* produces them and which *organ* excretes them from the body.

4) The diagram opposite shows some of the body's main organs.

   a) Name each of the *organs* A – H in the diagram.

   A *homeostatic organ* is one that helps to actually remove substances from the body, rather than just controlling the levels of substances indirectly.

   b) Which of the organs A - H are *homeostatic* organs?

   c) Which organ *continually checks* all the homeostatic conditions?

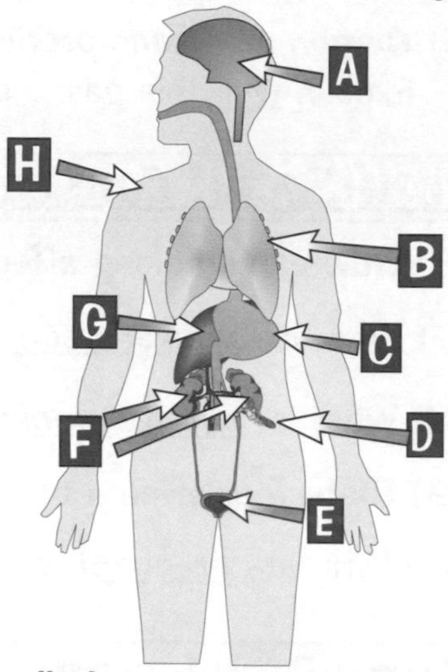

Controlling Internal Conditions

5) Name *four* internal conditions that the body's homeostatic controls try to maintain at optimal levels.

6) Humans are warm-blooded — that is our body temperature is controlled internally.

   a) What system *controls* the body's temperature?

   The part of the brain which monitors and adjusts temperature is called the *Thermoregulatory Centre*.

   b) If the core temperature of a human is *above* 37°C what *two* measures could this system use to lose heat? Describe how each measure takes heat *away* from the body.

   One of these heat-loss systems involves *losing water*.

   c) *What else* is lost in the water at the same time?

   d) In what two ways could the thermoregulatory system *increase* the temperature of the body if it dropped *below* 37°C?

Cold- and Warm-Blooded Animals

7) The table shows a comparison between air temperature and the body temperature of a reptile and a human.

   a) On the same axes, *plot a graph* of temperature (↑) versus time (→) for each of (a), (b) and (c).

   b) *Suggest why* the reptile's temperature was low between 12 noon and 4 pm.

Time	4am	8am	12 noon	4pm	8pm	Midnight
a) Human Body Temperature	37°C	37°C	37°C	37°C	37°C	37°C
b) Air Temperature	10°C	22°C	39°C	39°C	30°C	8°C
c) Reptile Body Temperature	7°C	19°C	10°C	10°C	19°C	7°C

   c) What happens to the *human's* body temperature throughout the day? What does this tell us about the *relationship* between air temperature and internal body temperature?

   d) *Many reptiles and snakes thrive in hot conditions. What would these creatures have to do if their summer habitat had *cold winters*?

Homeostasis and The Kidneys

Controlling the Glucose level of the Blood

8) *Controlling the blood-sugar level is part of homeostasis too.*

a) Which *two organs* are involved in controlling *blood-sugar* level?

b) Name the *two hormones* which serve as *messengers* between these two organs.

The hormones use a feedback mechanism to keep the blood-sugar level fairly constant.

c) What do we mean by a *feedback mechanism* of hormones?

d) Briefly *describe* how the feedback mechanism for maintaining blood-sugar level works.

Controlling the Amount of Water in the Blood

9) *Water is a major component of the blood.*

a) Name the hormone that *controls* the water content of the blood.

b) What *gland* produces this hormone?

c) What part of the brain *monitors* the blood's water content?

d) Copy and complete the flow diagram below for the two cases when (i) the blood is *too dilute* and (ii) the blood is *too concentrated*, by filling in the missing words.

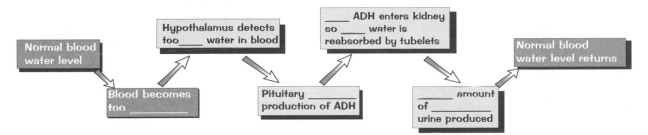

10) *The flow chart opposite shows the homeostatic process of regulating the amount of water and other substances in the blood. It is carried out by the kidneys.*

a) What is (1) – the process that *removes liquid* from the blood?

b) The kidney tubules adjust the amounts of water and *three other* substances in the blood. Name the three substances (2), (3) and (4).

c) What do we call (5)? One of the substances named in (b) is taken back *fully* into the bloodstream. Which one?

d) *What* is the waste liquid eventually produced by the kidney? What *three* things does it contain?

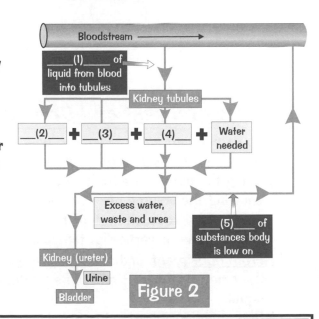

Figure 2

Top Tips: Homeostasis — another long word you'll need to know, so learn this definition: *Homeostasis* is the *maintenance* of a *constant internal environment* in the body. The point is that we have to get rid of waste, or it'll just pile up inside us and poison us — and we need to keep *ion* content, *water* content, *sugar* content and *temperature* at the right levels or our cells will stop working properly and we will die. Remember, homeostasis happens *automatically* — controlled by the *hypothalamus* and the *pituitary gland* in the brain. You've got to be able to describe how the *skin*, the *muscles*, the *kidneys*, the *liver*, the *pancreas* and the *lungs* are involved in homeostasis (look at pages 60, 76 and 78). This topic can be a bit complicated, so learn it all carefully.

Kidneys

How Kidneys Function

1) The kidneys are the body's filters. They adjust the levels of various substances in the blood and remove ones we don't need.
   a) What are the three main roles of the kidneys?
   b) What does the word excretion mean?

2) The diagram opposite shows part of the system involving the kidneys.
   a) Name the parts of the system A – F.
   b) How does the blood travelling through parts B and C differ?

3) There are approximately a million tube systems in a kidney.
   a) What is the name given to these tube systems.
   b) What surrounds each of them?
   c) Below is a diagram of a single tube system. The table opposite contains a description of each part.
   Match the labels (a) — (h) with their correct description 1 — 10.

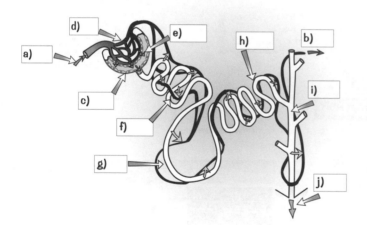

1. Branch of the renal artery — blood here requires "cleaning".	5. Glomerulus — a knot of capillaries that increases the blood pressure.
2. Glomerular filtrate — produced by the process of ultrafiltration.	7. Branch of renal vein taking away filtered blood.
3. First coiled tubule — glucose and amino acids reabsorbed back into blood here.	8. Second coiled tubule — selective reabsorption occurs here to prevent the loss of water and salts.
4. The Loop of Henlé — ion exchange allows sufficient water to be reabsorbed – depends on level of ADH in liquid.	9. Collecting duct — carries away waste liquid after reabsorption.
5. Bowman's Capsule — water, urea, ions and glucose are squeezed into here. Also supports knot of capillaries and leads to tubule.	10. Tubes leading to the bladder — carry away urine, the waste liquid consisting of urea and excess ions and water.

The rate of Sweat and Urine Production

4) An experiment was carried out on a person to see how much sweat and urine they produced at various temperatures. The results are shown in the table below.

a) Using the data in the table, draw a line graph showing the volume per hour of sweat and urine produced across a range of temperatures. (Plot volume/hr vertically, temperature horizontally)

b) From your graph find the temperature at which the amount of sweat and urine produced are equal.

c) How does an increase in air temperature affect:
   i) the amount of urine produced?
   ii) the amount of sweat produced?

d) Explain your answers to part c).

e) In some countries, temperatures can reach 40°C. From your graph estimate the amount of i) sweat and ii) urine that would be produced at this temperature.

f) Name one thing the people carrying out the experiment should have done to achieve an accurate result, and one way in which they could improve their experiment.

Air temp °C	Sweat produced (cm³/hr)	Urine produced (cm³/hr)
0	6	100
5	7	90
10	14	80
15	28	70
20	45	60
25	70	47
30	115	35
35	190	21

Kidneys

Regulating the Bloodstream

5) Substances are continually being reabsorbed and excreted by the kidneys to maintain the correct balance of constituents in the blood.
   a) What constituents are generally _reabsorbed_ by the kidneys and put back into the bloodstream?
   b) What substance is _excreted_ in the urine of diabetics?
   c) _Urea_ is a soluble compound found in the urine, but _where_ is it produced and _what_ is it made from?

6) The process of reabsorption of substances into the bloodstream requires energy, which is obtained from respiration.
   a) What _gas_ is needed for _respiration_ to occur?
   b) Where might the _kidneys_ get this gas from?

The Importance of Water to the Body

7) Maintaining the correct amount of water is vital to the body's functioning.

Intake (cm³)		Output (cm³)	
Food and drink	1850	Breathing	400
Respiration	A	Sweating from skin	600
		Urine from kidneys	1050
		Faeces from gut	150
Total taken in	2200	Total produced	B

   a) About what _percentage_ of the body is water?
   b) _Copy_ the _table_ opposite and complete it by filling in values for A and B.
   c) What do you notice about the _total intake_ and the _total output_? Explain your finding.

8) The body needs to constantly balance the water coming in against the water going out.
   a) What _hormone_ controls the amount of water in the body? Which _gland_ produces it?
   b) _Explain_ how this hormone controls the absorption and excretion of water in the kidneys.

9) What _ions_ are excreted if the blood contains _too much_ salt?

Kidney Failure

10) If a person's kidneys stop working, they can be helped out by an artificial kidney called a dialysis machine. The diagram to the right shows the process of dialysis and how the machine works.

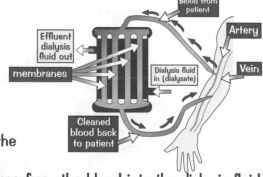

a) The dialysis fluid and the blood _cannot not be mixed_, so what type of _membrane_ must keep them apart?
b) _How_ are useful substances stopped from moving from the blood into the dialysing fluid?
c) Name an _excretory product_ apart from water that must pass from the blood into the dialysis fluid.
d) What _process_ allows this to occur?
e) _Name one_ substance that must stay in the blood.
f) Why do you think the blood and dialysis fluid flow in _opposing directions_ in the machine?
g) Why do red blood cells _remain_ in the blood and not pass into the dialysate liquid?
h) Explain why in cases of permanent kidney failure it would be better to have a _kidney transplant_ operation than frequent treatment with a dialysis machine.

Top Tips:
Lots of information on these pages, and two _important diagrams_ in Question 1. You need to know the diagram of the excretory system, and be able to name all the bits (take care not to mix up the ureter and the urethra). Remember, the kidneys have _three_ main jobs. You won't be expected to _draw_ a diagram of a nephron, but you _will_ have to _label_ one and say how it works. Remember — _ultrafiltration_ squeezes it all out, and _selective reabsorption_ lets the bits you want back in again — don't forget that big molecules like _proteins stay in the blood_ because they're too big to get through the capillary wall. Lastly, you do need to know about the two treatments for kidney failure.

Skin

The Body's Largest Organ

1) Use the diagram opposite, and the labels below it, to answer the following questions.

a) What is the _outer layer_ A of the skin called?

b) Some of the cells in A are _living_ and some are _dead_. _Why_ is this and _where_ in the layer are each found?

c) What happens to the cells at the _top_ of this outer layer?

d) If skin is _rubbed_ for a period of time, for example when wearing new shoes, what happens?

e) Which _part_ of the skin is labelled B?

f) i) What substance is _stored_ in part C of the skin?
   ii) What is the _function_ of this substance?

g) i) What is part D in the diagram? What is _lost_ through part D?
   ii) From _where_ does gland E absorb this substance?

h) Part G is a special muscle. What is its name?

i) i) Name F — the part of the skin mainly responsible for _temperature control_.
   ii) _Explain_ how it achieves this.

j) What part of the skin makes it sensitive to _stimuli_ in its surroundings? Name _two_ such stimuli.

k) Name part J. What does the substance it produces do?

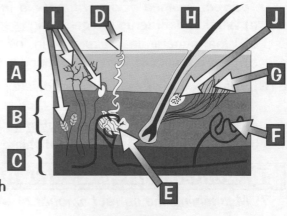

Epidermis | Fat Layer | Dermis | Hair | Sweat Pore | Blood Capillaries | Erector Muscle | Sweat Gland | Oil Gland | Receptor Cells

Temperature Control

2) _Normal body temperature is 37°C and this needs to be maintained as closely as possible. Because of this the body has a number of systems that allow it to lose or gain heat._ Copy the flow diagram and complete boxes (a) and (b) to show how the body can react to rising and falling temperatures.

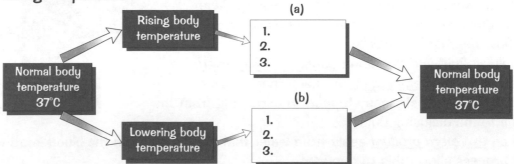

3) In an experiment a man drank an ice-cold drink and his body temperature fell from 37°C to 36°C. After 14 minutes his body temperature had returned to 37°C.

a) Explain _how_ this happens.

One of the ways the body reacts to lowered temperature involves contracting muscles.

b) Which _muscles_ contract and what is the _common name_ for this body reaction?

4) Draw sketch diagrams to show how the skin reacts when it is (i) _hot_ and (ii) _cold_.

5) a) Why does vigorous exercise tend to _increase_ body temperature?
   Our body temperature will often rise when we are ill.
   b) Where does the _extra heat_ come from?

6) Why do we feel _cooler_ on a hot, dry, windy day than on a hot, humid, calm day — even if the temperature is the same on both days?

Skin

The Function of Skin

7) The boxes below show components of the skin and their functions. Match each of the components A-G with the correct function 1-7.

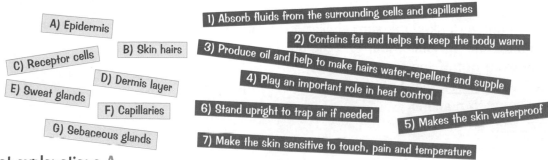

A) Epidermis
B) Skin hairs
C) Receptor cells
D) Dermis layer
E) Sweat glands
F) Capillaries
G) Sebaceous glands

1) Absorb fluids from the surrounding cells and capillaries
2) Contains fat and helps to keep the body warm
3) Produce oil and help to make hairs water-repellent and supple
4) Play an important role in heat control
6) Stand upright to trap air if needed
5) Makes the skin waterproof
7) Make the skin sensitive to touch, pain and temperature

8) Look at explanations A — D in the box to the right. Which one is the correct cause of greasy skin?

> A — a thin epidermis, B — over-active sebaceous glands,
> C — too many sebaceous glands, D — too much fat in the diet.

9) In an experiment class members took their body temperatures as follows:

Body temperature in °C
36.7 36.8 37.1 36.9 36.9 37.0 37.3 36.8 37.2 37.1

a) What was the _average_ temperature for this class?
b) What is the _normal_ human body temperature?
c) Why is it necessary for body temperature to be kept fairly _constant_?
d) What happens if the body temperature gets too _high_?
e) What is the name of the process in which the body temperature and metabolic rate _lower_ so much that eventually we fall into a coma?

10) From the following word list _select_ one to fit each sentence (each word is used only once).

Dark	narrowed	vasoconstriction	sneeze	pale
widened	vasodilation	shiver	red	

During cold weather our skin looks _____. This is because our arterioles have _____. This is called _____. The hairs on our skin stand up on end and we may also _____. When we are hot our skin looks _____. To lose heat the arterioles have _____. This is called _____.

The Composition of Skin

11) What is the name of the _substance_ in the epidermis that causes the brown colour of skin?

12) _Explain_ the causes and possible treatments of: a) acne b) sunburn.

13) What _protein_ is found in the skin cells that allows them to form a tough protective layer against the entry of foreign bodies?

Top Tips: Skin is pretty essential stuff. Believe me, you're better off with grubby spotty skin than with no skin at all. Remember, you need skin for _three_ reasons — to stop you _drying up_, to stop germs _getting in_, and to help control your _temperature_. Don't forget the _three_ things the skin _does_ to help control temperature — with the _hairs_, the _sweat_ glands and the _blood supply_. No prizes for guessing that you need to _learn the diagram_ in Question 1 and be able to name all the bits and say what they do.

Classification and Variation

Species

1) All organisms on this planet belong to groups called _species_.

   a) How can you tell if two organisms belong to the same _species_?

   b) A horse and a donkey are very similar animals. They can even mate and produce young. _Why_ are the horse and the donkey _not_ of the same species?

   c) Give two _features_ that both horses and donkeys have in common with humans.

Kingdoms

2) All living things can be placed into five groups called Kingdoms.

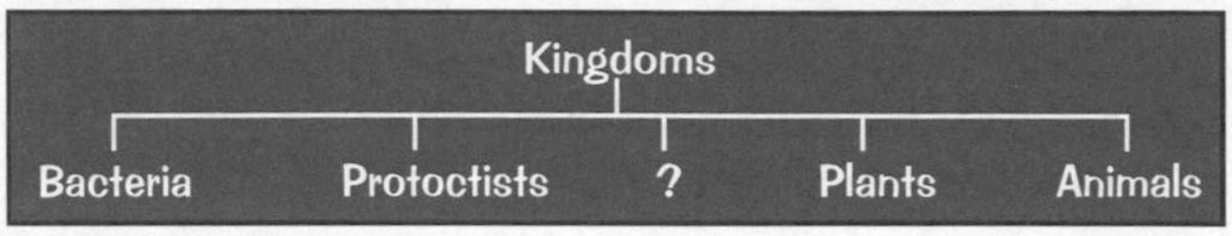

   a) Which Kingdom is _missing_?

   b) Give two features of plant cells.

   c) Name one example of a _protoctist_.

   d) State one _difference_ between bacteria and all the other Kingdoms.

   e) i) Why are viruses _not_ included in the Kingdoms above?

      ii) What are the _features_ of viruses?

      iii) How does reproduction in viruses _vary_ from reproduction in living things?

3) The diagram opposite shows part of the animal kingdom and how it is divided into smaller groups.

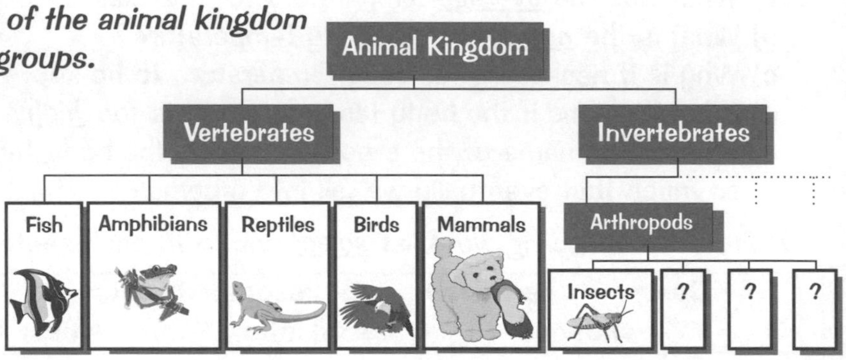

   a) An insect is an _arthropod_.

      i) Name one other example of an _arthropod_.

      ii) Give one _feature_ of this animal.

   b) Give one feature of _each_ of the vertebrate groups.

   c) State one feature that is _only_ found in: i) Fish, ii) Reptiles, iii) Birds, iv) Mammals.

The Binomial System

4) A man called Linnaeus devised a system where living things were given two names. This is known as the binomial system. Humans have the scientific name _Homo sapiens_. The group _Homo_ included other human-like animals in the past. Only humans are included in the group called _sapiens_ (this means "wise"). The idea is similar to giving a person a first name and a surname.

   a) i) Which part of the scientific name is _equivalent_ to the surname?

      ii) _Explain_ your answer.

   b) _Homo sapiens_ is a mammal. _Give_ two features of mammals.

5) There are four different groups of plants.

   a) State one _feature_ that all plants have.

   b) Give one feature that is _only found_ in:
      i) conifers, ii) flowering plants.

   c) For ferns and mosses: i) _State one_ feature they have in common, ii) _Give one_ difference.

Classification and Variation

Proportions of the different Animal Groups

6) *The pie charts show the proportions of all animals that live on the planet.*

a) i) Which is the most <u>common</u> type of animal found on this planet?

ii) Which is the most <u>numerous</u> arthropod?

b) Give one <u>example</u> of an animal found in each of the following groups: i) arachnids, ii) crustaceans, iii) myriapods.

c) State one <u>feature</u> for each of these groups:
i) arachnids ii) crustaceans iii) insects iv) myriapods.

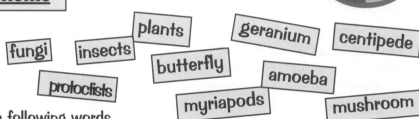

The Grouping of Organisms

7) <u>Copy</u> out the words and <u>match</u> the correct <u>organism</u> with the group it belongs to.

fungi insects plants geranium centipede butterfly amoeba protoctists myriapods mushroom

8) <u>Complete</u> the blanks with the following words.

binomial   birds   chlorophyll   classified   cloudiness   conifers   hyphae
insects   jointed   living   nucleus   Protoctists   reproduce   splitting

All living things can be _____ into five Kingdoms. These are: Animals, Bacteria, Fungi, Plants and _____. The system used for naming organisms is the _____ system. Bacteria have cell walls but do not possess a _____. They also reproduce by _____ into two. Bacteria cause _____ in a liquid. Fungi do not have _____, but produce spores and have thread like _____. Viruses are not _____ things. They are smaller than bacteria and are surrounded by a protective protein coat. Viruses can only _____ by infecting other living cells. The largest animal group is the arthropods. These include _____, crustaceans and myriapods. All arthropods have _____ legs. The vertebrates include fish, amphibians, reptiles, _____ and mammals. There are four main groups that plants are divided into. They are mosses, ferns, _____ and flowering plants.

Mastering Taxonomy

9) *Which <u>group</u> of living things does each of the following description apply to?*

i) It has a cell wall but <u>no nucleus</u>.

ii) The body is made up of a mycelium of <u>hyphae</u> and produces spores.

iii) It has a simple stem but <u>no</u> xylem and phloem and produces spores.

iv) This animal has <u>three</u> body regions, three pairs of legs and wings.

v) This is a <u>cone bearing</u> plant.

Top Tips:
Classification (also called taxonomy) can seem a bit confusing at first glance, but if you're able to learn the five Kingdoms: <u>Plants</u>, <u>Animals</u>, <u>Bacteria</u>, <u>Fungi</u> and <u>Protoctists</u> then you're over half way to understanding this topic. You're quite likely to be asked questions about how the Animal and Plant kingdoms are <u>sub-divided</u>. Remember there are <u>five vertebrate groups</u> and <u>four plant groups</u>, and learn the main features of each.

Variation in Plants and Animals

1) When Alex looked at the ivy plant growing up the oak tree in his back garden, he was surprised how much the size and colour of the leaves varied.

   a) What _kind_ of variation is this?

   b) What can _affect_ the size and colour of ivy leaves?

   c) Ivy plants have a very distinctive shape to their leaves. All mature leaves have the same shape.
   Is this genetically _or_ environmentally determined?

Human Characteristics

2) The jumbled list below shows different human characteristics.

   a) Which _of these characteristics show:_
      i) _continuous_ variation?
      ii) _discontinuous_ variation?

   b) _Which of the features are:_
      i) affected by the _environment_?
      ii) _not_ affected by the environment?

   c) Give the characteristic _least_ affected by inheritance.

   d) Choose any one feature and explain _how_ it is affected by the environment.

   Mass   Eye Colour   Fitness (measured by resting pulse)   Hair Colour   Intelligence   Height

3) Identical twins have the same genes, so they are genetically identical. The table shows four people, identified by the letters a, b, c and d.

   a) i) _Use_ the information in the table to identify which two people are identical twins.
      ii) _Explain_ your answer.

   b) From the table, give one _characteristic_ which shows:
      i) continuous variation.
      ii) discontinuous variation.

| | | Person | | |
Characteristic	a	b	c	d
Have a sun tan	✔	✔		
They are male	✔	✔	✔	
They are female				✔
Can tongue roll	✔		✔	
Normal hair colour is brown	✔	✔	✔	✔
Have bleached white hair			✔	✔
Have brown eyes	✔	✔	✔	

4) Place ticks in the table below to give the correct information for each of the human characteristics.

Characteristic (human)	Type of Variation		Affected by Environment	
	Continuous	Discontinuous	Yes	No
Birth weight				
Skin colour				
Blood group				
Hand span				
Eye colour				
Haemophilia				

5) People belong to one of these four blood groups: _A, B, AB_ and _O_. Use the words from the list to _fill in_ the spaces.

discontinuous	environmental	inherited	range

Blood groups show _____ variation. Here, there is not a wide _____ of characteristics. Our blood group is _____ and is not altered by _____ conditions.

Variation in Plants and Animals

Continuous or Discontinuous Variation

6) *There are two types of variation: continuous and discontinuous.*

a) i) Which *type* of variation is shown in graph A?
   ii) Give a *reason* for your answer.
   iii) Explain what the "*norm*" labelled on the graph shows.
   iv) What do we call this *type* of distribution of numbers?

b) i) Which *type* of variation is shown in graph B?
   ii) Give a *reason* for your answer

c) In each case, suggest what the characteristic could be.

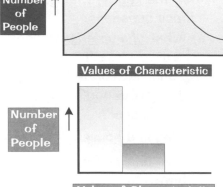

Environment versus Genetics

7) *Complete* the blanks using the following words.

discontinuous	environmental	genetically
inherited	mutation	range	variation

Differences between living things are called variation. There are two types of _____, continuous and _____ variation. Continuous variation, such as height, skin colour and hair colour show a range of characteristics. This type of variation is _____ determined but _____ conditions can modify the appearance of plants and animals. Discontinuous variation does not show a wide _____ of characteristics. Examples of this type of variation include blood groups and ear lobes. Characteristics can be passed on to the next generation and are called _____ characteristics. When genes change, this is called _____. This causes a new characteristic which will be passed on to the offspring.

Varieties of Plants

8) *Aisha collected marigold seeds from one of the plants in her garden. She gave half of the seeds to her friend James. The following year each of them grew their seeds in their garden. They were both surprised to find that when the plants grew, they looked so different. The table below shows the appearance of the two sets of plants.*

a) Give two reasons for the differences in the *appearance* of the two sets of plants.

b) i) All the plants had orange flowers, although the shade of orange varied from plant to plant. What determines the *colour* of the flowers?
   ii) What kind of *variation* is this?

Aisha's plants 🌼	James' plants 🌿
Leaves — dark green and no blotches	Leaves — pale green with brown blotches
Stems — tall and thick	Stems — short and thin
Large flowers	Small flowers

9) *There is variation in the clover plants that grow in this country. The two types of clover plants are: cyanogenic (which produces the poison cyanide) and acyanogenic which does not produce cyanide.*

a) What *type* of variation does clover show here?

b) What advantage does a plant have by being *cyanogenic*?

c) *Sometimes, plant breeders deliberately set out to produce plants that are different. This is often done by irradiating seeds (exposing them to radiation).*
   i) What does *irradiating* the seeds do to them?
   ii) Why do plant breeders want to produce *different* plants?

Top Tips: There's plenty of variation on these pages, so you won't get bored... Remember, variation can be *environmental* or *genetic* — and it's usually a little bit of *both* — but don't forget the *four important exceptions* which you need to learn. Variation can also be *continuous* or *discontinuous* — learn some examples of each.

Classification Keys

Animal Keys

1) Use the *key* on the right to answer these questions:

a) What *characteristics* does a housefly have to make it:
   i) an invertebrate?
   ii) an arthropod?
   iii) an insect?

b) Why is a housefly *not* an arachnid?

c) Give one *feature* that amphibians, birds, fish, mammals and reptiles have in common.

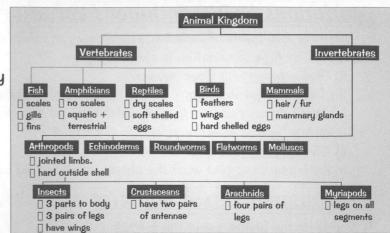

d) Use the key to *classify* these animals.

e) i) Why is *size* rarely used in keys?
   ii) Why is *colour* often avoided?

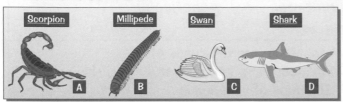

2) Using the information shown in the diagram opposite, design a key for identifying the five animals.

Keys involving Plants

3) The Venn diagram on the right tells you what the features of a moss plant are.

a) Use the other information below to decide *which* of the plants, A - D, is a moss.

b) Using this information *produce a key* for the plants below:

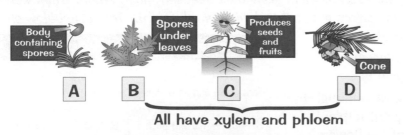

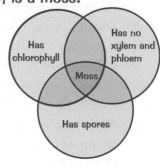

c) If we relabelled the circle which says "*has no xylem and phloem*" to "*has xylem and phloem*", *which plants* would the diagram apply to?

d) Produce the *same type* of diagram for an insect.

Evolution of the Five Kingdoms

4) This diagram on the right shows how the five kingdoms evolved over millions of years.

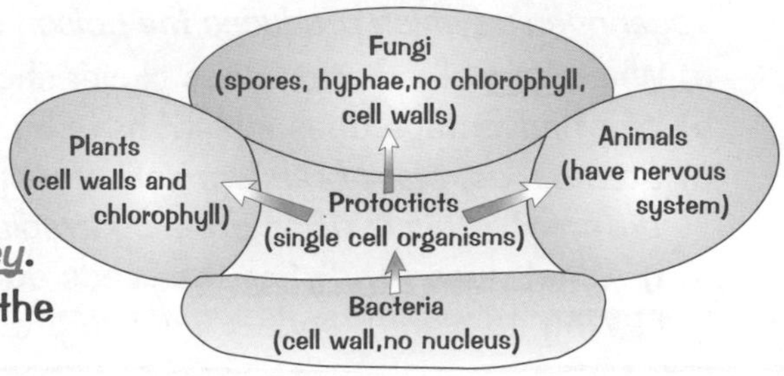

a) Use the information in the diagram to *produce a key*.

b) Give one *example* of a living thing found in each of the Kingdoms Fungi and Protoctists.

c) *Use your key* to place each of the organisms below into a Kingdom.

d) State one *similarity* and one *difference* between these two organisms.

Classification Keys

Invertebrate Animals Key

5) *This is a key for six invertebrate animals.*

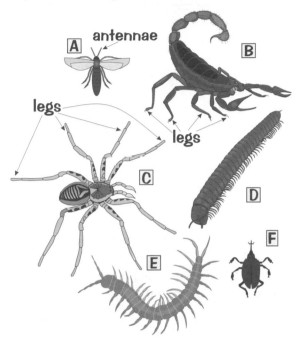

1)	More than 3 pairs of legs................go to 2
	3 pairs of legs.................................go to 4
2)	Have 4 pairs of legs ....go to 3
	More than 4 pairs of legs ....go to 5
3)	End of body is rounded ....spider
	End of body is pointed....................scorpion
4)	Wings not hidden by wing case ....midge
	Wings hidden by wing case ....weevil
5)	Has one pair of legs per segment .....centipede
	Has two pairs of legs per segment ....millipede

a) *Use the key* to identify each of the animals.
b) *Which* of the animals above are:
   i) arachnids?
   ii) insects?
   iii) myriapods?

Keys Involving Leaves

6) a) *Use the information* in the leaf key below to complete the results table (bottom right).

1)	Leaf is long and thin ....go to 2
	Leaf is not long and thin ....go to 3
2)	Leaf has short, visible petiole ....Osier
	Leaf does not have visible petiole ....Scots pine
3)	Leaf is hairy ....Woolly willow
	Leaf does not have hairs......................go to 4
4)	Leaf has "toothed" edge ....English elm
	Leaf does not have "toothed" edge ....Italian maple

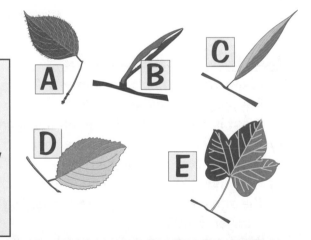

b) What *features* do *all* plant cells possess?
c) Give one feature they have in *common* with Bacteria.

Leaf	Which key numbers are used?	Name
A		
B		
C		
D		
E		

Top Tips: Another section that looks a bit confusing, but go through it carefully and it won't seem half as bad. Remember, a *key* is just a *series of steps* that *distinguish* between different categories of organism by their *features* — eventually you narrow it down to just one organism or group of organisms. When you make a key, the trick is to find features that split organisms as equally as possible into two groups at each stage.

Genetics

A Genetic Crossword

1) *Complete* the crossword by answering these questions.

Across

3 - A male gamete. (5,4)
6 - Sex of child when an ovum joins with a Y carrying sperm cell. (4)
8 - A sex cell. (6)
11 - Contains genes. (10)
12 - The genes that are present. (8)
14 - The allele that is masked when a dominant gene is present. (9)

Down

1 - Has a nucleus, cytoplasm and a membrane. (4)
2 - One of two genes that control a particular characteristic. (6)
4 - The bases in DNA are this. (6)
5 - Genetically identical individual. (5)
7 - The condition when the two alleles are different. (12)
8 - A section of DNA that controls a particular characteristic. (4)
9 - Produced when a sperm joins with an egg. (6)
10 - Cell division which produces sex cells. (7)
13 - Egg cells. (3)

Cells and Chromosomes

2) *In humans, the haploid number is 23.*
   a) Are *sperm* haploid or diploid?
   b) What is the *process* that joins the sperm and egg cell called?
   c) How many chromosomes are there in the zygote of a *human*?
   d) How many chromosomes are there in the zygote of a *crayfish* whose *diploid* number is 112?
   e) What *type* of cell division produces the sperm and egg cells?
   f) What type of cell division is used for *growth*?
   g) What is a *gamete* ?

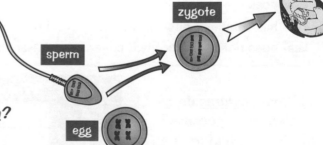

develops into a baby

zygote

sperm

egg

Genes and Chromosomes

3) *The diagram shows the arrangement of four genes on a pair of chromosomes.*
   a) Give the *letters* of two genes that are alleles.
   b) State which of the *alleles* are:
      i) dominant,
      ii) recessive.
   c) "B" determines brown eye colour and "b" blue eye colour. What *colour* eyes would the person with the arrangement in the diagram have? *Explain* your answer.

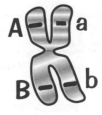

A — — a

B — — b

SECTION FIVE — GENETICS AND EVOLUTION

Genetics

It's all in the Genes!

4) *Complete* the sentences by choosing the correct word from inside the brackets.
  a) The allele that determines a characteristic in the heterozygous state is (*dominant* / *recessive*).
  b) Another name for a sex cell is a (*gamete* / *zygote*).
  c) The genes a person has is called his (*genotype* / *phenotype*).
  d) The middle of a chromosome is called the (*centromere* / *chromatid*)
  e) Chromosomes are made up of (*carbohydrates* / *DNA*).
  f) In humans, a cell that has all **46** chromosomes is said to be (*diploid* / *haploid*).
  g) Our bodies use (*meiosis* / *mitosis*) to produce cells for growth.
  h) The (*heterozygous* / *homozygous*) condition is when two alleles are the same.
  i) An egg cell is an example of a (*gamete* / *zygote*).
  j) Genetically identical organisms are (*clones* / *mutations*) of each other.
  k) Random combination of chromosomes in meiosis creates (*mutation* / *variation*).

5) *Match* up the dark boxes with the correct pale boxes, on the right. An example has been done for you.

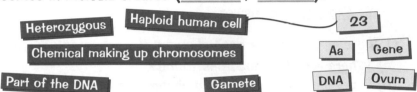

Cross Fertilization

6) *On the right is a genetic diagram* showing how two pea plants could share their genes by cross fertilization.
  a) What do we *mean* by:
    i) phenotype?
    ii) genotype?
  b) What do we mean by "*F1* generation"?
  c) What is the *ratio* of their:
    i) genotypes?
    ii) phenotypes?
  d) Give all the possible *genotypes* from the alleles T and t.
  e) What are the possible *phenotypes* from these alleles?

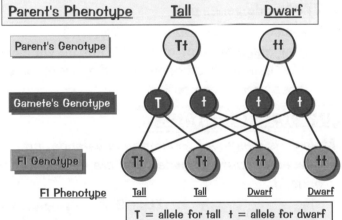

7) Fill in the blanks with the following words.

| alleles | centromere | chromatids | DNA | dominant |
| gene | heterozygous | homozygous | recessive |

Chromosomes are made of _____. They are made up of separate arms called _____. The middle part of chromosomes, connecting the chromatids is called the _____. A _____ is a section of DNA. Different versions of the same gene are called _____. The allele which determines the characteristic is said to be _____. The one whose characteristic is masked is _____. When both alleles are the same, we say the individual is _____. Whereas, when they are different the individual is said to be _____.

Top Tips:
The really important thing here is to *learn the words*. If you don't know what they mean, you won't be able to understand the rest of this topic. In Question 4, there are a lot of words that *look* similar but mean very *different* things.

Genes, Chromosomes and DNA

Chromosomes and Genes

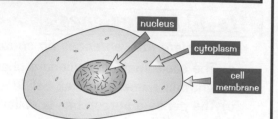

1) *This is a typical animal cell.*
   a) What <u>part</u> of the cell are chromosomes found in?
   b) If this was a human cheek cell, <u>how many</u> chromosomes would there be inside it?
   c) What is the <u>chemical</u> that chromosomes are made of?

2) *Two frog zygotes, A and B, from completely different parents had their nuclei removed. The nucleus from A was given to zygote B.*
   a) What does the nucleus <u>contain</u>?
   b) i) Would the frog that develops from B resemble the parents of A or B?
      ii) <u>Explain</u> your answer.

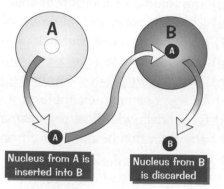

3) *The diagram on the right shows a typical chromosome.*
   a) <u>Where</u> are chromosomes found?
   b) Label parts A and B of the chromosome.
   c) i) What is the <u>chemical</u> that is found in the chromosome?
      ii) How is this chemical <u>arranged</u>?
   d) i) What is a <u>gene</u>?
      ii) What do genes do?
   e) *Chromosomes are found in pairs.*
      i) <u>How many</u> pairs of chromosomes do we have in each of our body cells?
      ii) One pair of chromosomes is the sex chromosomes. What <u>name</u> is given to each of these chromosomes?

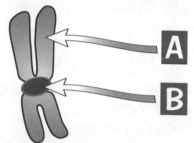

Gene Flow Diagrams

4) *Melanin is a pigment (colouring substance) produced in the body. It is this substance that is produced in your skin when you are exposed to sunlight. This reaction shows how melanin is produced.*

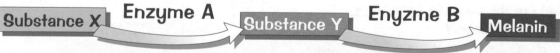

The enzymes drive the reactions. That is to say, Enzyme A catalyses the conversion of substance X to substance Y and Enzyme B catalyses the conversion of substance Y to melanin.

   a) Suggest a <u>reason</u> why some people cannot produce melanin.
   b) Can a person who does not produce Enzyme A produce melanin? <u>Explain</u> your answer.
   c) Enzymes are made up of proteins. What <u>carries</u> the information for making proteins?

5) *Some varieties of wheat have more gluten than others. Gluten is a protein. Bakers particularly like wheat which is high in gluten because this type of wheat produces better dough.*

<u>Complete</u> the flow diagram to show how gluten is made.

Genes, Chromosomes and DNA

Characteristics of DNA and Chromosomes

6) _Complete_ the blanks using the following words.

| chromosomes | cytoplasm | diploid | divide | DNA |
| genes | haploid | nucleus | protein | sex |

The _____ contains the chromosomes that carry the genes. Every species has its own number of _____. In humans, it is 23 pairs (46 chromosomes). This is called the _____ number. Every cell in the body of living things has the diploid number, except the _____ cells. These cells have the _____ number which in humans is 23 chromosomes. The _____ on the chromosomes control the characteristics of organisms. Chromosomes are made up of a double helix of _____. A gene is a portion of DNA that acts as a code for the production of a particular _____. Proteins are assembled in the _____ of a cell. When cells _____ the DNA has to be copied accurately.

7) _The diagram shows the connection between DNA and several characteristics._

   a) i) _Where_ is the DNA found in cells?
      ii) Where are _proteins_ made in the cell?

   b) _Fill in_ the spaces to complete the diagram.

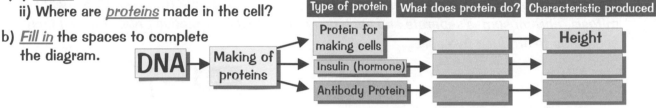

   c) What happens to the _characteristics_ if the DNA is changed (mutated)? _Explain_ your answer.
   d) _Milk has proteins in it. The proteins contained in milk vary for different mammals. Why is this?_

There are 23 Pairs of Human Chromosomes

8) _The figures below show the chromosomes of a human male and female._

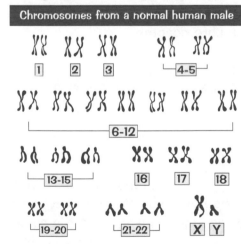

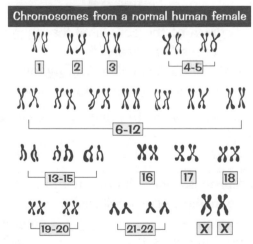

   a) What is the _difference_ between the two sets of chromosomes?
   b) Why do we talk in terms of _pairs_ of chromosomes?
   c) What are the "_arms_" of the chromosome called?
   d) i) _How many_ chromosomes do we have in each body cell? ii) _Where_ in the cell are the chromosomes found?
   e) i) What is the name of the _chemical_ that makes up chromosomes? ii) How is this chemical _arranged_?
      iii) What do we call _sections_ of this chemical?

Top Tips:
All the stuff on these pages is _very important_. You really do need to know what a _chromosome_ is and _where_ in the cell it's found and what a _gene_ is, what it's _made of_ and what it _does_. Remember that portions of DNA that have the code for one protein are called genes. Don't forget, we have _pairs_ of chromosomes, one from each parent.

Mitosis and Meiosis

Reproductive Cells

1) *The diagrams show the two types of cell division.*

   a) Name cell division types A and B.

   b) Give one *difference* not shown in the diagram between cell divisions A and B.

   c) Cell division B is sometimes referred to as reduction division. *Explain* the reason for this.

   d) i) Give *two uses* for cell division A.

   ii) What is cell division B used for?

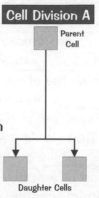

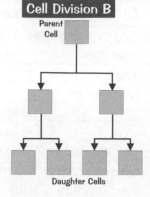

What Happens To Chromosomes

2) *The graph below shows what happens to chromosomes during mitosis. Curve A shows the mean distance between centromeres and their corresponding pole (the end of the cell). During mitosis, chromosomes separate and each half moves to its respective pole. The cell then separates to produce two cells.*

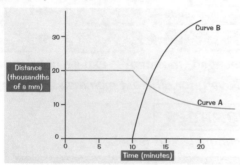

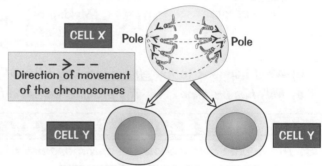

   a) On the diagram of the cell, label the *centromere* of one chromosome.

   b) What does curve B represent?

   c) i) In one of the cells labelled Y, *draw* the appearance of the chromosomes.

   ii) If cell X was undergoing meiosis, how would the chromosomes in cell Y differ?

3) Use the following words to *complete* the blanks.

asexual	exact	gametes	parent	reduction	two

Mitosis is a process used during growth and _____ reproduction. Each chromosome in the original cell makes an _____ copy of itself. When this type of division is complete, _____ daughter cells are produced, each having the same chromosome number as the _____cell. Meiosis is a _____ division — this means that the number of chromosomes in the original cell is reduced (halved). This process is used in the production of male and female _____. Meiosis involves some reassortment of genetic material, so producing variation.

4) State whether the following statements apply to *meiosis* or *mitosis*.

   a) Produces *haploid* cells.

   b) Produces identical cells to *parent* cell.

   c) At the end of division, two *daughter* cells are produced.

   d) Used in *sexual* reproduction.

   e) Used in *asexual* reproduction.

Mitosis and Meiosis

The Cell Divisions

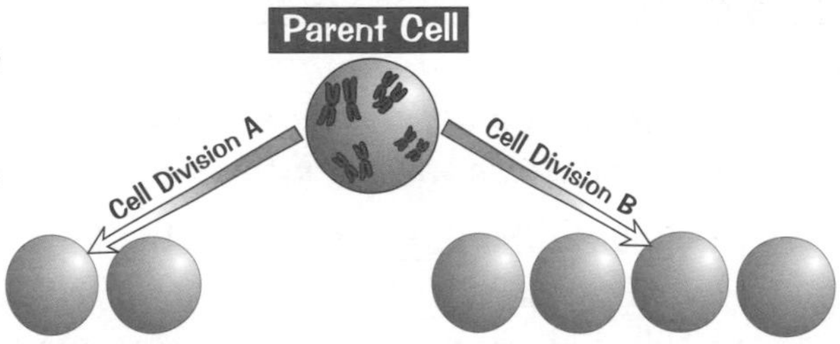

5) The diagram opposite shows the difference between
   the two types of cell division.

   a) Name the _type_ of cell division involved in A and B.

   b) _Where_ does A take place in the human body?

   c) _Where_ does B take place:

   i) in a plant?   ii) in the human body?

   d) If the diagram represents cell division in the _human_ body, how many chromosomes are there
   in one of the cells produced from :   i) division A?   ii) division B?

6) By taking cuttings, many plants are produced from one plant.

   a) Cuttings are genetically identical. What do we call genetically
   identical _individuals_?

   b) What type of _cell division_ is used when cuttings grow into new,
   mature plants?

   c) The cuttings eventually grow flowers. The flowers produce
   pollen and egg cells. What type of cell division is used in the
   production of _pollen_ and _egg cells_?

   d) When pollen fuses with an egg cell, a seed is formed. What
   type of cell division is used during _germination_?

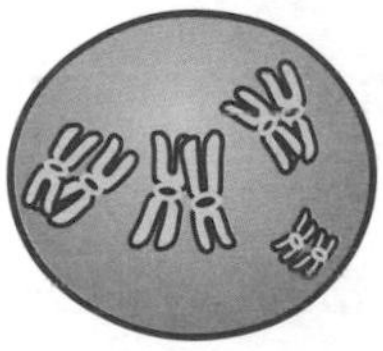

7) This is a drawing from the body cell of a fruit fly.
   Draw how the chromosomes would appear in:
   a) the egg cell of a fruit fly.
   b) a muscle cell after it has divided.

8) Plants like strawberry plants can reproduce in two ways.
   They can use flowers and also runners.
   a) i) What type of cell division is involved in
          producing the runner?
       ii) What is this _type_ of reproduction called?

   b) The gametes that produce the seeds are made
      in the flower.
      i) What type of _cell division_ is involved in this
      form of reproduction?
      ii) What is this _type_ of reproduction called?

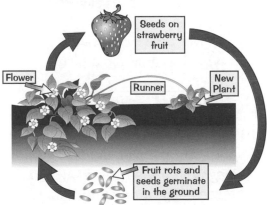

Blood Cells in the Human Body

9) The human body is forever replacing existing cells. For example, red blood cells are made in
   bone marrow. 200,000,000,000 are made every day!

   a) By _what process_ are red blood cells made in the bone marrow?

   As red blood cells mature, they lose their chromosomes.

   b) _Name_ two types of plant cells that _lose_ their contents
   (including the chromosomes) as they mature.

   c) Explain the _advantage_ to each of these cells of losing their cell
   contents.

   d) What advantage is there for a red blood cell _not_ to have any
   chromosomes?

   e) Where are chromosomes _located_ in a cell?

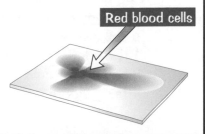

Red blood cells

SECTION FIVE — GENETICS AND EVOLUTION

Mitosis and Meiosis

Cell Division in Animals and Plants

10) If we were to study the different parts of an animal's body, we would find areas of cell division for growth around all the organs of the body. If we did the same thing in plants, only specific areas will be dividing in this way.

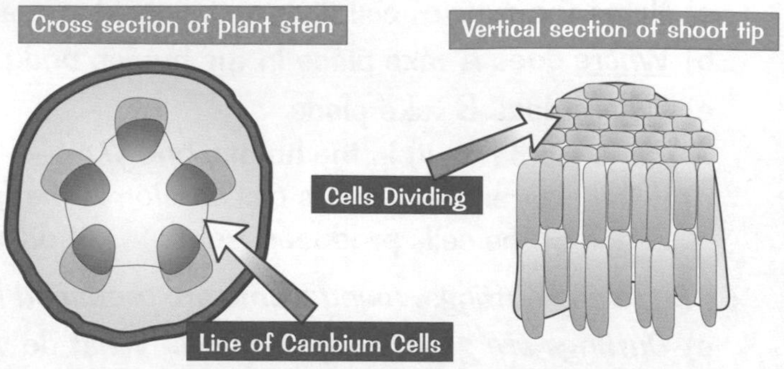

a) What is the _name_ given to this type of cell division?

b) Using the information in the diagrams on the right, _explain_ the _effect_ on the plant when:
i) The cambium cells divide.
ii) The shoot tip cells divide.

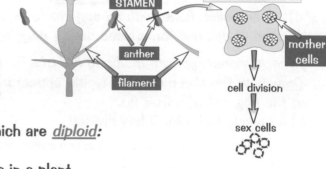

Cross section of plant stem

Vertical section of shoot tip

Cells Dividing

Line of Cambium Cells

c) Cell division also occurs in the reproductive parts of a plant. One of the reproductive parts is the anther. This is part of the stamen which is the male part of the plant.

i) What is the _female_ reproductive organ of a plant called?

ii) Where are the plant _reproductive_ organs located?

Plant Reproductive Organs

STAMEN

anther

filament

Section through anther

mother cells

cell division

sex cells

d) The mother cells in the anther produce the sex cells.
i) What is the _name_ given to these sex cells?
ii) What _type_ of cell division produces them?

e) State which of these cells are _haploid_ and which are _diploid_:
i) anther mother cells   ii) sex cells
iii) cells in a petal   iv) stem cells in a plant
v) liver cells in an animal   vi) testes cells in an animal
vii) pollen grains in a plant

Active Cell Division

11) In genetic engineering, a human gene can be placed in the chromosome of a bacterium. The diagram on the right shows how we use this technology to produce insulin.

a) What does _insulin_ do in the human body?

b) Bacteria divide very quickly. One bacterium can produce 14 million in 24 hours by splitting in half every 30 minutes.

i) By what _process_ do the bacteria divide?
ii) _How many_ bacteria are produced every time a cell divides?
iii) If bacterial cells divide every half hour, how many cells would be produced from one cell after _5 hours_?

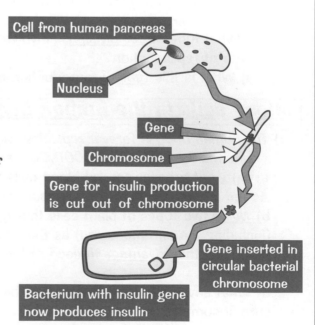

Cell from human pancreas

Nucleus

Gene

Chromosome

Gene for insulin production is cut out of chromosome

Gene inserted in circular bacterial chromosome

Bacterium with insulin gene now produces insulin

Mitosis and Meiosis

12) _Complete_ the information in the spaces in the table.

Organism	Number of chromosomes in a body cell	Number of pairs of chromosomes	Number of chromosomes in each gamete	Haploid number	Diploid number
Fruit Fly	8				
Kangaroo	12				
Rye Plant	20				
Chicken	36				
Mouse	40				
Humans	46				
Crayfish	200				

13) _Diagram **A**_ shows the stages involved in cell reproduction by _mitosis._
    Diagram **B** shows the stages involved in cell reproduction by _meiosis._

For each diagram, _describe_ in your own words what is happening at _each_ of the _numbered_ stages.

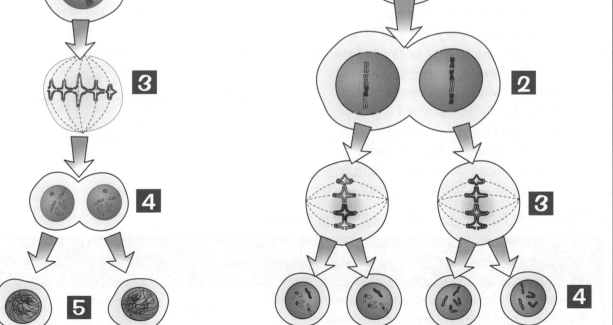

Diagram A

Diagram B

Top Tips: You've gone a whole four pages without a top tip, so I bet you're looking forward to this one. The big thing here is remembering the difference between mitosis and meiosis. _Mitosis_ gives you _two identical diploid cells_ — it's used for growth, repair and asexual reproduction. Now, _meiosis_ gives you _four different haploid cells_ and is _only_ used for the production of sex cells. You need to know _how_ the chromosomes split up in the cell and whether they are _shuffled_ or _replicated_ in each type of cell division. Learn and enjoy.

Fertilisation

From Sex Cells to a Baby

1) The diagram shows the progress from sex cells to a baby.

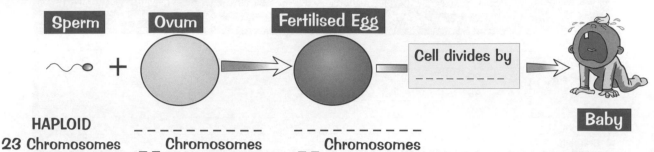

Sperm   Ovum   Fertilised Egg   Cell divides by _____   Baby

HAPLOID
23 Chromosomes   _ _ Chromosomes   _ _ Chromosomes

a) *Complete* the five spaces in the diagram above.
b) Name the *reproductive* organs that produce:
   i) sperm cells.
   ii) ova.
c) What *word* also means sperm and egg cells?
d) What is *another* name for a fertilised egg?
e) What do we call the *process* where sperm and egg cells join together?
f) *Where* does fertilisation take place in the body of the human female?

Combining the Parent Cells

2) Gametes are haploid, that is to say, they carry only one chromosome from each pair found in their parent cells.

a) *Complete* the diagram below by drawing how the chromosomes in the fertilised egg would appear after the joining of the sperm and ovum.
b) i) Where are *sperm cells* produced?
   ii) Where are *egg cells* produced? 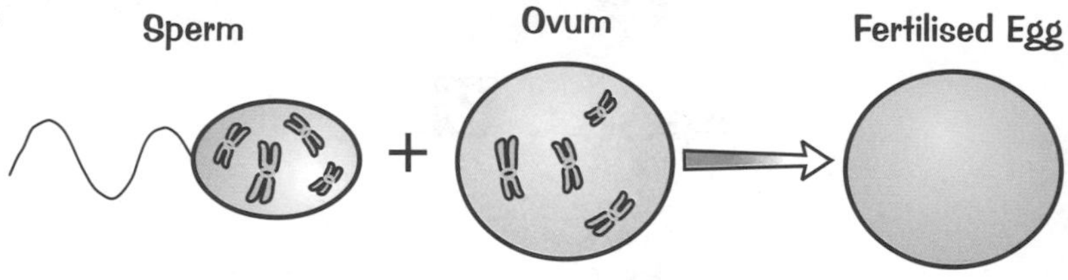
c) How is information carried from:
   i) the *father* to the child?
   ii) the *mother* to the child?
d) Chromosomes appear in pairs.
   i) What word describes a *matching* pair of chromosomes?
   ii) How many *pairs* of chromosomes do we have in our body cells?

Sperm   Ovum   Fertilised Egg

3) Use the following words to *complete* the blanks.

| children | chromosome | diploid | egg | fertilisation | gametes |
| meiosis | ova | ovaries | sperm | testes | variation |

Sexual reproduction involves the production of _____, followed by _____.
Random combination of chromosomes in _____ creates genetic _____ amongst
the sperm and _____ cells produced. The random fusion of gametes gives rise to
variation in the _____. The male gametes are the _____ cells and the female
gametes are the egg cells (also called _____). Male gametes are produced in the
_____ and female gametes are produced in the _____. The gametes
contain one _____ from each homologous pair. When fertilisation occurs, these
chromosomes come together to produce the correct _____ number, which in humans is 46.

4) *Define* the following words.

      diploid   fertilisation   gamete   haploid   ova   ovaries   zygote

Fertilisation

The Sperm Cell and Egg Cell

5) *The sperm cell can be divided into three parts, the head, the middle piece, which is packed with mitochondria, and a tail.*

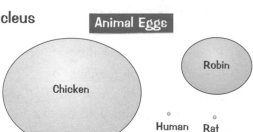

A Sperm Cell

head

tail

middle piece

a) Give *one function* for each part of the sperm cell.

b) *The nucleus of a sperm has a mass which is half the mass of other nuclei in the human body.*

   i) What is contained in the *nucleus* of a sperm cell?

   ii) Give one reason for the *difference* in mass of the nucleus in a sperm cell and the nuclei of other body cells.

c) Why are sperm *much* smaller than egg cells?

d) Why do mammals have such *small* eggs compared to birds?

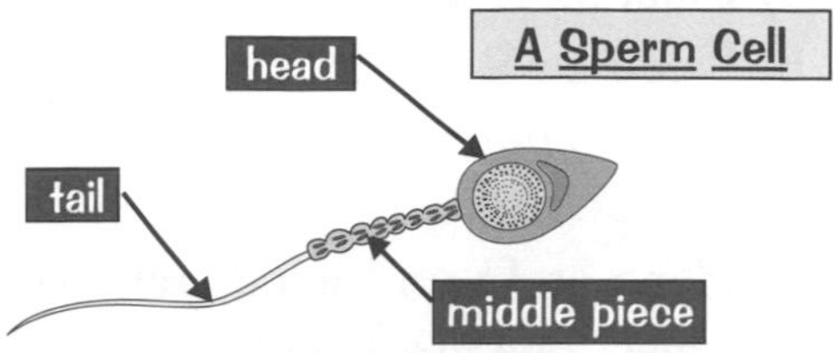

Animal Eggs

Chicken

Robin

Human   Rat

6) *Match* the appropriate descriptions on the left to the terms on the right.

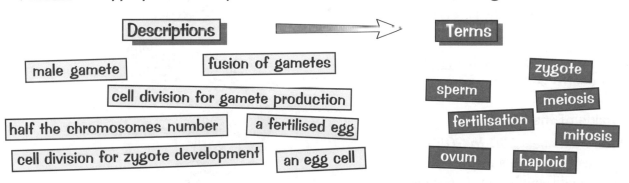

Descriptions

male gamete

fusion of gametes

cell division for gamete production

half the chromosomes number

a fertilised egg

cell division for zygote development

an egg cell

Terms

zygote

sperm

meiosis

fertilisation

mitosis

ovum

haploid

7) *Complete* the spaces in this table of information about the various features of sex cells in animals.

Feature	Applies to egg/sperm cell	Significance of feature
Very small	sperm	
Relatively large	egg	
Has a tail		
Has haploid nucleus		

8) *Complete* the sentences below by choosing a word from *inside* the brackets.

a) Gametes are produced by (*meiosis* / *mitosis*).

b) Another name for sex cells is (*gametes* / *zygotes*).

c) Chromosomes occur in (*homologous* / *homozygous*) pairs.

d) Gametes are (*diploid* / *haploid*) cells.

e) Another name for an egg cell is an (*ovary* / *ovum*).

Top Tips: Plenty of new words here for you to learn, and some you'll already know. You know the basic point that fertilisation is when a sperm and an egg cell fuse together, but remember that two *haploid* cells are fusing together to form a *diploid* cell. Don't forget that *after* fertilisation, this cell is called a *zygote* — a funny name, but you need to know it. One last thing — you do need to know *how* variation in the *children* comes about.

Human Reproduction

Female Reproductive System

1) *The diagram on the right shows the front view of the female reproductive system.*

a) Label structures A to E.

b) Place an S on the diagram to show where *sperm* is released during sexual intercourse.

c) Place an O on the diagram to show where *ova* are released.

d) Place a G on the diagram to show where the *baby* grows.

e) Place an F on the diagram to show a likely place for *fertilisation*.

f) Draw arrows to show the *pathway* of a sperm cell to an egg cell.

g) Why are women with blocked oviducts *infertile*?

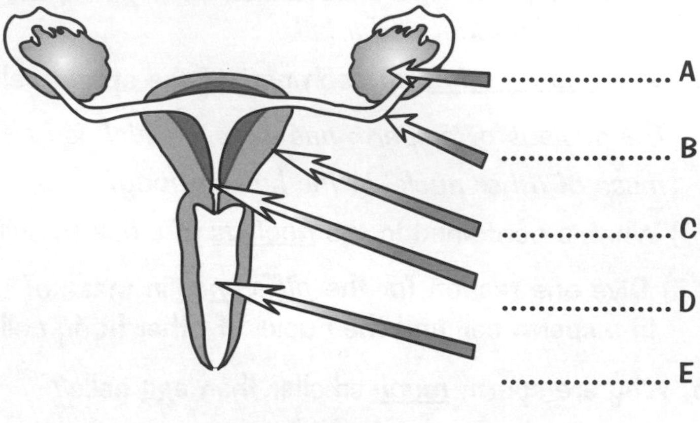

.... A

.... B

.... C

....................D

.... E

Male Reproductive System

2) *The diagram below shows the side view of the male reproductive system.*

a) Label structures A to G.

b) What structures make and store *sperm* cells?

c) Draw arrows to show the *route* of a sperm cell from where sperm are made to the outside of the body.

d) *A man releases 200 to 300 million cells when he ejaculates. Explain why such a large number of sperm cells are produced.*

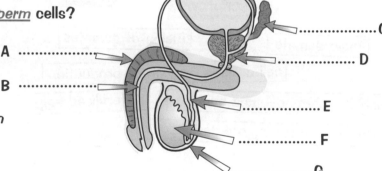

A ....

B ....

....................C

.... D

.... E

.... F

....................G

e) *The sperm duct uses its muscles to push sperm cells along by contracting and relaxing muscles.*

i) *Where else* in the body are muscles used in this way?

ii) What is the name of this *process*?

3) *Complete* the table.

Structure	Function	Male or Female?
Glands (prostate and seminal vesicle)		
Ovaries		
Oviducts / Fallopian tubes		
Penis		
Scrotum		
Sperm Ducts		
Testes		
Uterus		

SECTION FIVE — GENETICS AND EVOLUTION

Human Reproduction

Human Fertility

4) The graphs below show the human menstrual cycle and associated events.

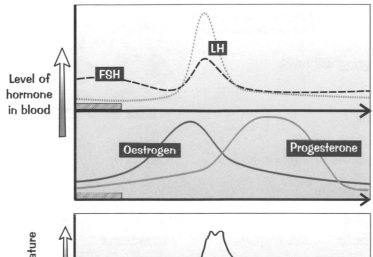

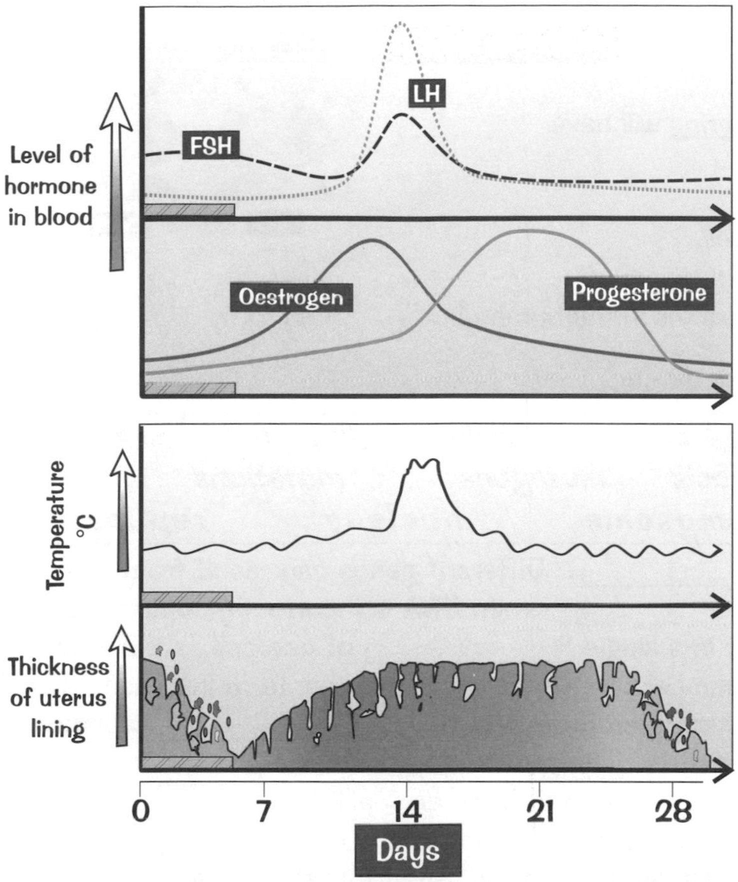

a) Why are days 1 to 5 shaded?

b) i) Why does the lining of the womb _thicken_?
   ii) What _helps_ to bring this change about?

c) i) When is _ovulation_ (egg release) most likely to occur?
   ii) What _hormone_ stimulates the release of the egg?
   iii) Where is this hormone _produced_?

d) The rhythm method of contraception involves avoiding sexual intercourse between days 13 to 17.
   i) _How_ does this work?
   ii) Why is this _not_ an effective method of contraception?
   iii) Use the information in the graph to explain how women can use their _body temperature_ to help them identify when they are releasing an egg.

e) i) What does FSH do? ii) What produces FSH?

f) Some women are given FSH as part of their fertility treatment. _How_ does this work?

g) The combined contraceptive pill contains progesterone and oestrogen hormones. Both of these hormones can inhibit FSH production.
   i) What is a _hormone_?
   ii) How does the combined contraceptive pill _prevent_ women from getting pregnant?

h) Draw a line on the progesterone curve to show what happens to the _level_ of _progesterone_ if a women conceives (gets pregnant) on day 18 of her menstrual cycle.

5) a) The uterus is made of thick muscle. Explain the _reason_ for this.
   b) The cervix is only the width of a milk straw but becomes flexible during labour. _Why_ is this?
   c) What is the function of the _fluid_ in the amniotic sac?
   d) i) Name _two substances_ a baby gets from its mother.
      ii) _Where_ does the exchange of substances occur?

Top Tips:
In the Exam, you can be asked to label diagrams of the male and female reproductive systems. You need to know where _sperm_ and _eggs_ are produced, _where_ fertilisation occurs and _how_ the sperm get there (and it's more complicated than just "during sexual intercourse"). The slightly tricky bit here is learning all those hormones in the menstrual cycle. Remember _what_ happens at each stage, and _why_ and _how_ it happens.

SECTION FIVE — GENETICS AND EVOLUTION

98

Mutations

What Causes Mutations

1) *Cells A and B are taken from two different Drosophila flies (fruit flies). One cell is normal, the other has a mutation which gives the fly misshapen eyes. Cell A has the mutant gene.*

a) What is a *gene*?
b) How can *mutations* like this one arise?
c) i) Is there any chance that this fly's *offspring* will have the mutation?
   ii) *Explain* your answer.
d) *This mutation started in a fertilised egg cell.*
   i) How did other cells end up with the *mutant* gene?
   ii) Give *one* example of the effect of mutations in the human body.

Drosophila Fly Eyes | Mis-shapen eyes | Normal eyes

Cell A   Cell B

2) *Complete* the blanks by using the following words.

antibiotics	beneficial	carcinogens	divide	genetic	sex
harmful	ionising	mitosis	mutagens	mutations	
naturally	neutral	chromosome	nucleus	replication	

A mutation is a change in a gene or a _____. Different genes can result from such a change. Mutations can occur _____ when DNA is incorrectly copied during _____. Gene mutations may start in a single _____ of one cell. As the cells _____ to produce more cells, the number of cells carrying the new form increase. The chance of _____ occurring can be increased by exposure to _____ radiation, X-rays, ultra-violet light and also certain chemicals. The greater the dose, the greater the chance of mutations occurring. Chemicals that cause mutations are called _____ and include substances found in cigarette smoke. Such substances are called _____ because they can increase the chance of people having cancer. Most mutations are _____. If mutations occur in _____ cells, the children may develop abnormally. This can result in early death. Mutations that occur in body cells can cause uncontrollable cell division (_____), resulting in cancer. Some mutations are _____ in their effects, causing no apparent harm or benefit to the individual. On rare occasions, a mutation can be _____, increasing an organism's chances of survival. Bacteria mutating has definitely benefited them by giving them resistance to the _____ we use against them. Mutation is the source of _____ variation. Changing by acquiring new forms of old genes is how living things have evolved by natural selection.

Beneficial and Harmful Mutations

3) a) *Mutations can be both beneficial and harmful. Give one example of each.*
   b) *The blue colour in budgies appeared as a mutation in green budgies. This does not affect the survival of budgies in any way.* What does this tell us about *some* mutations?

4) *The graph on the right shows the relationship between the amount of ionising radiation and the number of recessive, lethal (deadly) alleles induced in the sperm cells of a mouse.*
   a) *What* does the graph show us?
   b) i) What does *ionising radiation* do to genes?
      ii) What is an *allele*?
   c) Besides ionising radiation, *what else* can cause similar effects?

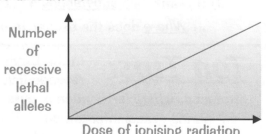
Number of recessive lethal alleles / Dose of ionising radiation

SECTION FIVE — GENETICS AND EVOLUTION

Mutations

Side-effects from X-Rays

5) *X-rays are used regularly in hospitals, mainly for looking at possible fractures in bones.*
   a) i) Why are hospitals reluctant to X-ray _pregnant_ women?
      ii) Why are the _early_ stages of pregnancy particularly important?
   b) Why do hospitals monitor _how often_ we are X-rayed?
   c) What _precautions_ are taken when we are being X-rayed?
   d) Why is more care taken when X-raying _younger_ people?

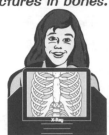

Natural Radiation

6) *In parts of the country where homes have been built above granite, the number of cancer cases is higher than average. This is due to radon gas that is released from underground and builds up in people's houses.*
   a) *People that have houses built above granite areas often have special air extraction fans inside them. Explain the _reason_ for this.*
   b) *What is _cancer_?*
   c) *What part of our cells does _radon_ affect?*

Mutations in Animals

7) *Ancorn sheep have very short legs. These first appeared in the flock of a farmer in the eighteenth century. The farmer decided that these sheep would be easier to control because they would not be able to jump over the walls of their enclosure.*
   a) How can a normal sheep _produce_ an ancorn lamb?
   b) What _caused_ the change to happen?
   c) i) Is this change an _advantage_ to the sheep?
      ii) _Explain_ your answer.
   d) *All the different breeds of dogs we have with us today originated from the wolf.*
      i) _Name_ some features that dogs have today that are not found in the wolf.
      ii) What happened in wolves to _produce_ these features?

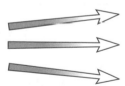

Summary Questions

8) _Select_ the correct word or words from inside the brackets to complete the sentences.
   a) Mutations (_are always_ / _can be_) harmful.
   b) Cancer is the result of cells dividing uncontrollably (_by meiosis_ / _by mitosis_).
   c) Mutations occur naturally when (_chromosomes replicate_ / _proteins are made_).
   d) Cigarette smoke contains (_mutagens_ / _mutations_) that can increase the chance of an individual having cancer.
   e) Mutations are the mechanism for the gradual change that is called (_evolution_ / _mitosis_).
   f) A mutation is when there is a mistake in the (_DNA_ / _protein_).
   g) A mutation is a change to a gene or (_a chromosome_ / _the cytoplasm_).
   h) A mutation in reproductive cells (_can be very harmful_ / _is not harmful_).

Top Tips: Sounds like a big scary thing, this mutation. Remember that a mutation is a fault in the DNA which happens _naturally_ when chromosomes are copied. You need to know the _factors_ which increase the chance of mutations happening. Don't forget, there can be _neutral_ and _beneficial_ effects of mutations _as well as_ harmful ones.

X and Y Chromosomes

Pairs of Chromosomes

1) _Complete_ the lines by filling in the missing information.

a) _Kidney cell from a man:_   has **22** pairs of chromosomes + __ __ chromosomes

b) _Kidney cell from a woman:_   has **22** pairs of chromosomes + __ __ chromosomes

c) _An egg cell:_   has **22** chromosomes + __ chromosome

d) _A sperm cell:_   has __ chromosomes + __ or __ chromosome

e) _A zygote which produces a girl:_   has __ chromosomes + __ and __ chromosomes

f) _A zygote which produces a boy:_   has __ chromosomes + __ and __ chromosomes

g) _A kidney cell from a boy suffering from Down's Syndrome:_   has __ chromosomes + __ and __ chromosomes

h) _A kidney cell from a girl suffering from Down's Syndrome:_   has __ chromosomes + __ and __ chromosomes

2) _Cells_ A _and_ B _are male and female reproductive cells._

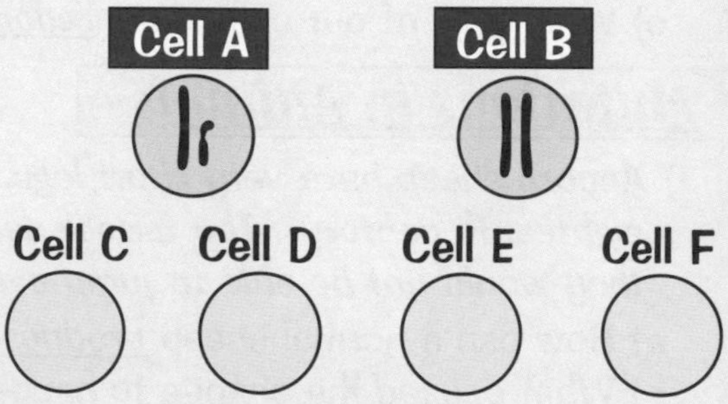

a) _Label_ the two sex chromosomes in cells A and B. Which cell is _male_ and which _female_?

b) _Where_ are cells A and B found in the body?

c) Cells A and B undergo cell division to produce the gametes C, D, E and F. _Complete_ these cells to show the sex chromosomes.

d) What are _male_ gametes and _female_ gametes called?

e) What type of cell division produced cells C, D, E and F?

f) What is the _total_ number of chromosomes in each of the cells A, B, C, D, E and F?

g) State which cells are _haploid_ and which are _diploid_.

Sex Inheritance

3) a) _Copy_ and _complete_ the diagram which shows how sex is inherited.

b) Work out from the diagram the _ratio_ of boys to girls.

c) _A couple have one child, Janet. The couple are convinced that their next child will be a boy because they already have a daughter._ Is this true? _Explain_ your answer.

d) Genotypes of offspring can also be worked out with a checkerboard type diagram (sometimes called a Punnett Square) _Complete_ the diagram to the right.

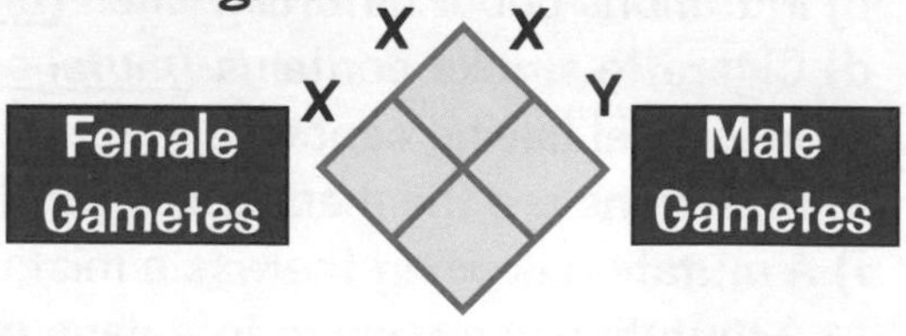

Parents' Phenotype :	_____	_____
Parents' Genotype :	X X	X _
Gametes' Genotype :	X X	X _
Childrens' Genotype :	_ _ X Y	X X _ _
Childrens' Phenotype :	____ ____	____ ____

Female Gametes   X   X   Y   Male Gametes

4) _In the old days, kings have been known to behead their wives for not giving them sons._

a) What sex chromosomes do _sperm_ cells have?

b) What sex chromosomes do _egg_ cells have?

c) i) Is it the man's or woman's gametes that _determine_ the sex of the child?

ii) _Explain_ your answer.

Chop off her head!!

SECTION FIVE — GENETICS AND EVOLUTION

X and Y Chromosomes

Chromosomes in Humans

5) a) *Explain* why it is possible for a couple to have four children, all daughters.

   b) *Christine is pregnant with her first baby.* What is the *chance* of Christine having a son? *Explain* your answer.

6) *This is a diagram of the chromosomes found in the body cells of a boy.*

   a) *Identify* and *label* the chromosomes that determine sex.
   b) What chromosomes determine sex in a *girl*?
   c) *Girls and boys pass their sex chromosomes into their sex cells.*
      i) What are the *sex cells* of boys and girls?
      ii) *Where* are these sex cells produced?
      iii) What *process* produces sex cells?

7) Use the following letters to complete the blanks. Letters may be used more than once.

X	XX	XY	Y

Men produce two types of sperm cells. Half contain an _____ and the other half contain a _____ chromosome. Eggs produced by women always contain an _____ chromosome. If an X chromosome bearing sperm combines with an egg cell, the zygote will have _____ chromosomes. This combination produces a baby girl. If a Y chromosome bearing sperm joins with an egg cell, the zygote will have _____ chromosomes. This will develop into a baby boy.

Male gamete	Female gamete		Zygote	Sex of child
sperm	+ ○	→	○	Girl
sperm	+ ○	→	○	Boy
sperm (X)	+ ●	→	●	- - - - -
sperm	+ ○	→	○ (Zygote splits)	Identical twins (girls)
sperm	+ ○	→	○	- - - - - } Non-identical twins
sperm (Y)	+ ○	→	○	Boy

8) Using the diagram on the left answer the following questions.

   a) *Complete* the inside of the circles to show the chromosomes that are *present*.

   b) Indicate the sex of children *not already* indicated.

Chromosomes in Birds

9) *Birds also have X and Y chromosomes that determine sex. In birds, unlike humans, the male is XX and the female is XY.* Use this information to *complete* the diagram.

Parents' Phenotype :	—————		—————
Parents' Genotype :	X X		X Y
Gametes' Genotype :	X X		X Y
Childrens' Genotype :	— — — —		— — — —
Childrens' Phenotype :	——— ———		——— ———

Top Tips: It's the X and Y chromosomes that determine whether you're male or female. Remember that *XX* chromosomes are needed to be *female*, and *XY* to be *male*. You need to be able to draw a diagram that shows that there's a *50:50 chance* of having girls or boys. Don't forget, birds have the X and Y chromosome the other way around.

SECTION FIVE — GENETICS AND EVOLUTION

Monohybrid Crosses

Crossbreeding Mice

1) The diagram shows a cross between a black male mouse and a brown female mouse.
   a) What does _homozygous_ mean?
   b) Why are some genes _represented_ by "B" and others by "b"?
   c) Explain _why_ B and b are alleles.
   d) _The F1 are all heterozygous black._
      i) What does F1 _stand for_?
      ii) What does _heterozygous_ mean?
   e) i) Which allele is _dominant_?
      ii) _Explain_ what dominant means.
   f) i) What does _genotype_ mean?
      ii) What does _phenotype_ mean?

Parents' Phenotype :	Homozygous Black Male	Homozygous Brown Female
Parents' Genotype :	BB	bb
Gametes' Genotype :	B B	b b
Offsprings' Genotype :	Bb Bb	Bb Bb
Offsprings' Phenotype :	All Heterozygous Black	

   g) _Two individuals from the F1, a male and a female, are taken and mated._
      i) Use a checkerboard type diagram to _show the cross_.
      ii) What are the _phenotypes_ and _genotypes_ of the offspring?
      iii) What is the phenotypic _ratio_ of the offspring?
      iv) What do we _call_ this generation?

Dominant and Recessive Genes

2) A brown eyed man married a blue eyed woman. The allele for brown eyes is dominant and that for blue eyes is recessive.
   (The father is heterozygous for the gene)
   a) What _letters_ would you use for the brown and blue alleles?
   b) On the diagram, _complete_ the cross by filling in the spaces.
   c) Which individuals are _homozygous_?

Parents' Phenotype :	Blue eyed mother	Brown eyed father
Parents' Genotype :	___	___
Gametes' Genotype :	___ ___	___ ___
Offsprings' Genotype :	___ ___	___ ___
Offsprings' Phenotype :	___ ___	___ ___

   d) How is it _possible_ for two brown eyed individuals to have a blue eyed baby?

3) Complete the blanks with these words.

| alleles | F1 | F2 | genotype | height | heterozygous |
| homozygous | | monohybrid | phenotype | recessive | |

In _____ crosses, we only cross for one characteristic, such as _____ in pea plants or colour in mice. Each gene has two different forms — these are called _____. The allele whose characteristic is masked in the presence of a dominant gene is _____. If two alleles are the same, we say they are _____ and if they are different, they are _____. The word _____ refers to the appearance or the physical characteristic that results, whereas _____ refers to the alleles present. In genetic crosses, we talk about different generations. The _____ represents the children and the _____ the grandchildren.

4) The Stewarts are a Scottish family from Glasgow. Margarite Stewart is a dark haired woman who has an auburn haired son called Cameron. Half of Margarite's brothers and sisters have dark hair, the other half have auburn hair. Auburn hair is recessive to dark hair.
   a) What _letters_ would you use to _represent_ the two alleles?
   b) What _genotypes_ do the following have:
      i) Margarite? ii) Cameron? iii) Margarite's two parents? iv) Margarite's dark haired brother? v) Margarite's auburn haired sister?

SECTION FIVE — GENETICS AND EVOLUTION

Monohybrid Crosses

Tracing People who can Taste PTC

5) This is a pedigree chart showing how the ability to taste the chemical PTC is inherited. PTC is
a chemical that tastes bitter to some people but is tasteless to others. The ability to taste
this substance is determined by a dominant allele.

a) i) Is person 9 a _male_ or _female_?
   ii) Is this person a _taster_ or _non-taster_?

b) i) What _letters_ would you use to
      represent the two alleles?
   ii) What is the _genotype_ of person 2?
   iii) How did you _work_ this out?

c) i) What is the _genotype_ of 4?
   ii) What is the _evidence_ for this?

d) Give one _example_ of a person who must be
   i) _homozygous_.
   ii) _heterozygous_.

e) Produce a _cross_ from 1 and 2 to _show_
   whether their offspring would be tasters
   or non-tasters.

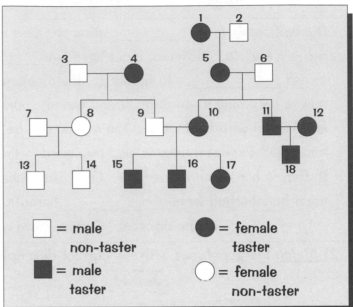

= male
non-taster

= female
taster

= male
taster

= female
non-taster

Crosses Of Plants

6) Gregor Mendel was an Austrian monk. He trained in mathematics and natural
history at the University of Vienna. On his garden plot at the monastery,
Mendel noted how characteristics in plants were passed on from one
generation to the next. The diagrams show two of the crosses that
Mendel carried out.

First Cross

Parents: Tall Pea plant   Dwarf Pea plant

F1 offspring: All tall Pea plants

Second Cross

Two pea plants from the F1 offspring are crossed

Parents: Tall Pea plant   Tall Pea plant

F2 offspring: Tall Tall Tall Dwarf

From the _first cross_:

a) i) Give the _genotypes_ of the dwarf
      and the tall parents.
   ii) Give the _genotypes_ of the F1 offspring.

From the _second cross_:

b) i) What is the _genotypic ratio_ of the F2
      offspring?
   ii) What is the _phenotypic ratio_ of the F2
      offspring?
   iii) Which individuals are _homozygous_?
   iv) Which individuals are _heterozygous_?

c) What _other characteristics_ in a pea plant
   could Mendel have experimented with?

Top Tips: Enough already with the confusing words. A _monohybrid cross_ means
you're crossing for just _one_ characteristic. You'll need to know how to
work out a cross. Remember that a _heterozygous_ individual displays the _dominant_ characteristic,
not something in between dominant and recessive. Don't forget that 3:1 ratio, and how you get it.

SECTION FIVE — GENETICS AND EVOLUTION

Cystic Fibrosis

What is Cystic Fibrosis

1) Use these words to _complete_ the blanks.

allele		both		carriers		digestive		genetic
	lungs		membranes		mucus		recessive	

Cystic fibrosis is a _____ disease. One in twenty people in this country carry the recessive allele. Sufferers must have two _____ alleles. Cystic fibrosis is a disorder of cell _____. In the lungs, the membranes produce thick sticky _____ which makes breathing more difficult and causes more infections to the _____. Infections are treated with antibiotics. The mucus can be removed by regular physiotherapy and massage. Excess mucus is also produced in the pancreas, causing _____ problems. Sufferers have a shortened life. Since the disease is caused by a recessive _____, it must be inherited from _____ parents. Parents who have the recessive allele are _____ of the disorder. Carriers have no ill-effects themselves.

2) _Match_ the genotypes with the correct description.

carrier

normal

sufferer

CC

cc

Cc

3) _The diagram below shows a cross between two unaffected people._

a) From the _diagram_, which individuals are:

i) carriers?
ii) sufferers?
iii) homozygous?
iv) heterozygous?

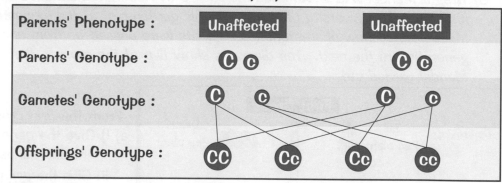

Parents' Phenotype :	Unaffected	Unaffected
Parents' Genotype :	C c	C c
Gametes' Genotype :	C c	C c
Offsprings' Genotype :	CC Cc	Cc cc

b) What do we mean by _carriers_?
c) _Draw this diagram_ in the form of a checkerboard.

Living with Cystic Fibrosis

4) _A major problem in the life of cystic fibrosis sufferers is that they produce thick mucus in their lungs. This makes breathing difficult because the mucus clogs up the lungs. Physiotherapy and breathing exercises are vital for sufferers to prevent the build-up of mucus in their lungs. Recurring chest infections are also a major problem. Because the pancreas also produces thick mucus, problems occur in digesting food in the small intestine._

a) Why do sufferers often need to take _antibiotics_?
b) Why do sufferers need _physiotherapy_ and _breathing exercises_?
c) Why is the _diet_ of a sufferer supplemented by _enzyme_ tablets?
d) Dnase is a mucus thinning drug. _How_ can this drug help sufferers?
e) Why are children suffering from cystic fibrosis often _weaker and smaller_ than other children?
f) _Pneumonia_ is also a disease which affects the lungs. What is the _difference_ between the cause of these two diseases?

Cystic Fibrosis

Origins and Symptoms

5) _Complete_ the sentences by selecting the correct word or words from inside the brackets.

   a) Cystic fibrosis is an (_infectious_ / _inherited_) disease.

   b) Cystic fibrosis is caused by a (_dominant_ / _recessive_) allele.

   c) Children can inherit the cystic fibrosis disease when (_both_/_one_) of their parents have the recessive allele.

   d) Sufferers of cystic fibrosis have breathing problems due to (_small lungs_ / _the excessive production of mucus_).

   e) The allele for cystic fibrosis is found (_equally in men and women_ / _only in men_).

Carriers and Sufferers

6) _The diagram shows a family who have been tested for the cystic fibrosis allele._

   a) Using appropriate letters, give the _genotypes_ of the mother and father.

   b) Will any of the children be _sufferers_?

   c) i) Can you say _which children_ will carry a recessive allele?
      ii) _Explain_ your answer.

   d) What is the _chance_ of Beth being a carrier?

   e) What _proportion_ of their children will be _normal_?

   f) i) From the _diagram_, can we tell whether both of the father's parents were _carriers_?
      ii) _Explain_ your answer.

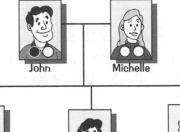

Father — John   Mother — Michelle

Beth   Jean   Nicholas

○ Recessive allele for Cystic Fibrosis
● Normal, dominant allele

The Likelihood of Developing this Disease

7) _If two carriers have children, there is a 1 in 4 chance of each child having the disease._

   a) _Show_ how this ratio is derived with a genetic diagram.

   b) _Can_ children suffer from the disease if only _one_ parent has a _recessive allele_?

   c) One in twenty people carry the allele for cystic fibrosis in this country. What do we mean by "_carrying_" the allele?

8) _Match_ up the statements on the _left_ with the correct answers from the _right_. There may be _more than one_ correct answer.

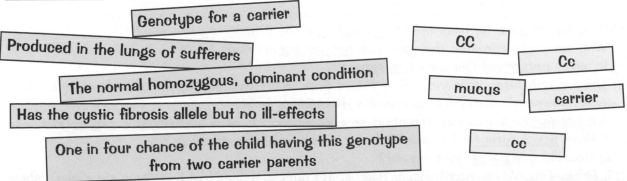

Genotype for a carrier

Produced in the lungs of sufferers

The normal homozygous, dominant condition

Has the cystic fibrosis allele but no ill-effects

One in four chance of the child having this genotype from two carrier parents

CC

Cc

mucus

carrier

cc

Top Tips: This nasty disease is a good example of a genetic disease that's caused by having _one_ faulty gene. This means you can work out a _monohybrid cross_, as in question 3. Remember, you'll be expected to know about the _symptoms_ as well as the genetics behind the disease in the Exam, so learn the facts on these pages.

SECTION FIVE — GENETICS AND EVOLUTION

Haemophilia

What is Haemophilia

1) *Complete* the blanks using the following words.

allele	blood	both	females	inherited
males	recessive	two	X	Y

Haemophilia is an _____ disease. The blood of sufferers does not clot and even minor cuts can be lethal from _____ loss. Knocks can also result in internal bleeding and bruising. Sufferers can be treated with a clotting agent called factor 8. This disease is a sex-linked disease because the _____ allele responsible for the condition is found on the _____ chromosome. The _____ chromosome is shorter and does not have an _____ for haemophilia. This means that in _____, only one allele on the X chromosome is needed to express the haemophilia condition. In _____, haemophilia is much rarer because _____ X chromosomes, _____ bearing recessive alleles are needed. The female zygote bearing $X^h X^h$ often does not develop.

Pedigree Chart of the British Royal Family

2) *The diagram is a pedigree chart of the British Royal Family showing how haemophilia is inherited. No-one before Queen Victoria's children had haemophilia in the Royal Family.*

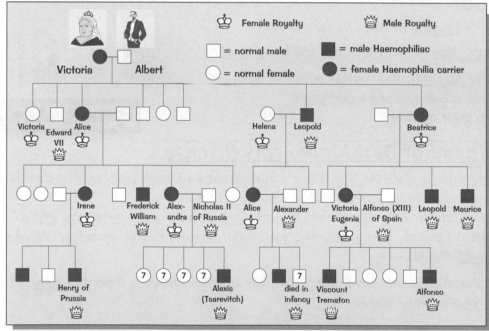

a) How did the gene for haemophilia *first appear* in the British Royal Family?

b) Why are we so *sure* that this gene was *not present* in Prince Albert?

c) In which *person* did this gene *first appear*?

d) *The present Queen descended from Prince Edward VII who married Princess Alexandra. There was no case of haemophilia in Princess Alexandra's family.*
   Is it *possible* for any of the present Queen's descendents to have *haemophilia*? *Explain* your answer.

e) i) From *which parent* did Prince Frederick William *inherit* haemophilia?
   ii) How did you *derive* your answer?

f) i) *Prince Leopold married Princess Helena. If Princess Helena had two dominant alleles, show* with a *genetic diagram* the possible genotypes and phenotypes of her children.
   ii) *Alice, Queen Victoria's granddaughter, married Prince Alexander. One of their sons died in infancy.* What is the *chance* that this child was a haemophiliac?

g) Using the diagram *explain* how the Spanish Royal Family have *also* ended up with this disease.

Haemophilia

The Genetics of a Disease

3) _Match_ the statements on the _left_ with the correct information on the _right_.

carrier male

normal male

haemophiliac male

normal female

carrier female

haemophiliac female

$X^H X^H$

$X^h X^h$

$X^H X^h$

$X^h Y$

$X^H Y$

combination does not exist

4) _A normal man marries a woman who is a carrier for haemophilia._

a) _Complete_ the spaces in the diagram.

Parents' Phenotype :	Normal male	Female carrier
Parents' Genotype :	_____	_____
Gametes' Genotype:	__ __	__ __
Offspring's Genotype:	__ __	__ __ __
Offspring's phenotype:	_____	_____ _____ _____

b) What is the chance of a daughter of this couple being a _carrier_?

c) What is the chance of a son of this couple being a _haemophiliac_?

d) _About 30% of people with haemophilia have no family history of this disease._
How does this occur?

5) _A genetic counsellor is advising two people of the chance of any of their children having_
haemophilia. The man is a haemophiliac and the woman is a carrier.

a) What is the _chance_ that any of their daughters will be born: i) carriers? ii) normal?

b) What _proportion_ of their _sons_ will be: i) normal? ii) sufferers?

Haemophilia Summary

6) Choose the _correct word_ or _words_ from inside the brackets to complete the sentences.

a) Haemophilia is a disease that a person (_catches_ / _inherits_).

b) Only (_men_ / _women_) can be carriers of haemophilia.

c) The allele for haemophilia is carried on the (_X_ / _Y_) chromosome.

d) Haemophilia results in the sufferer's blood (_clotting_ / _not clotting_) easily.

e) A (_man_ / _woman_) is more likely to be a haemophiliac.

f) The disease is the result of a (_dominant_ / _recessive_) allele.

g) A man needs (_one_ / _two_) recessive allele to be a sufferer.

h) Children who are sufferers from a family without history of the disease have a (_dominant_ /
mutated) allele.

Top Tips:
Another genetic disease for you to learn. Haemophilia is caused by a recessive allele. This time, though, _only_ the X chromosome carries the gene — the Y chromosome is too short. So, a _male_ will only have _one_ allele — and if it's the _recessive_ one, he will have the disease. Don't forget why female haemophiliacs are so rare.

Genetic Diseases

Sickle Cell Anaemia

1) Use the following words to complete the blanks:

alleles	blood	carrier	malaria	oxygen	protected	recessive	red

Sickle cell anaemia is a disorder of _____ blood cells. It is caused by a _____ allele. Being a _____ of this disorder can be an advantage in countries where _____ is prevalent. Carriers are _____ from malaria. The disease gets its name from the shape of the red _____ cells. Children who inherit two recessive _____ from their parents have red cells which are less efficient at carrying oxygen. The red blood cells also stick together in the blood capillaries. This deprives the body cells of _____ .

2) Map A shows the _distribution_ of the _sickle cell_ allele in Africa. Map B shows the _distribution_ of _malaria_ in the same geographical region.

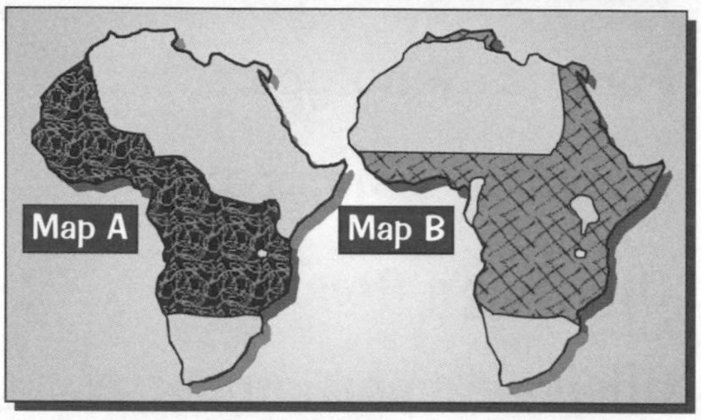

a) _Why_ are the distributions so similar?
b) Sickle cell anaemia is a _killer_ disease.
   i) What is an _advantage_ for people who are _carriers_ of the disease?
   ii) What is a _disadvantage_ for people who are _carriers_ of the disease?

Map A

Map B

Chances of Inheritance

3) _Two carriers marry and have three children._
   a) _Complete_ the spaces in the diagram.

Parents' Phenotype :	_____	_____
Parents' Genotype :	_____	_____
Gametes' Genotype :	__ __	__ __
Offsprings' Genotype :	____ ____	____ ____
Offsprings' Phenotype :	____ ____	____ ____

b) i) What is the _chance_ of one of the children being a sickle cell sufferer?
   ii) What _problems_ do sufferers of sickle cell anaemia experience?
c) _Carriers can enjoy good health, except that they can be anaemic._
   i) What is _anaemia_?
   ii) What is the _advantage_ of being a carrier?

Huntington's Chorea (also known as Huntington's Disease)

4) Use the following words to _complete_ the blanks.

allele	disease	dominant	mental	nervous	one

Huntington's Chorea is caused by a _____ allele. This means that _____ parent can pass on the disorder. A child has a 50% chance of inheriting the condition from one parent with a single dominant _____ . This disease affects the _____ system. Symptoms often develop when the person who has inherited the allele is over 35-40 years of age. The _____ causes involuntary movements and _____ deterioration. There is no cure and the condition progressively worsens.

5) a) _A man who is heterozygous for the condition marries a normal woman._
      What is the _chance_ of their _first child_ having the disease?
   b) _Diseases caused by a dominant allele are often expected to disappear._
      i) _Explain_ why.   ii) Why is Huntington's Chorea _not disappearing_?

Genetic Diseases

6) *The table shows the prevalence of Huntington's Chorea in a number of places. Tasmania with the highest number of cases has a small community. Suggest a possible reason why the number of cases of Huntington's Chorea is highest in Tasmania.*

The prevalence of Huntington's Disease (per million of the population)	
Cornwall	50
Tasmania	170
Victoria	45
USA	50

7) *Using the diagram on the right:*
   a) *Complete the spaces to show a cross between a heterozygous man and a woman who is homozygous recessive.*
   b) *What proportion of offspring from this cross are sufferers?*

Father   Mother

Parents' Phenotype : _____ _____

Parents' Genotype : _____ _____

Gametes' Genotype : ___ ___ ___ ___

Offspring's Genotype : ___ ___ ___ ___

Offspring's Phenotype : ___ ___ ___ ___

Down's Syndrome

8) Use the following information to *complete* the blanks.

| defects | diseases | eyes | 46 | 47 | learning |
| life | | meiotic | one | | two |

This disease results from children having _____ instead of _____ chromosomes. This is because sufferers have an extra number 21 chromosome (they have three instead of two). The extra chromosome occurs when an egg gets _____ instead of _____ number 21 chromosomes during _____ cell division. People with Down's Syndrome have _____ difficulties. They also have _____ which slant slightly upwards and outwards, a flat face, short fingers and a small stature. Down's Syndrome people also have sight, hearing and heart _____ , and are more susceptible to certain _____. These children have a shortened _____.

9) *The diagram to the right shows how Down's Syndrome is inherited.*
   a) i) Where is the *"mother's cell"* found in the human body?
      ii) Where is the *"father's cell"* found in the human body?
   b) What *type* of cell division produces the gametes?
   c) What *mistake* has occurred?

10) How does a mother's *age* affect her chances of having a Down's Syndrome child?

The relationship between a mother's age and the chances of having a Down's Syndrome child	
Mother's age	Chance of having a child with Down's Syndrome
25	1 in 1,400
40	1 in 110
45	1 in 30

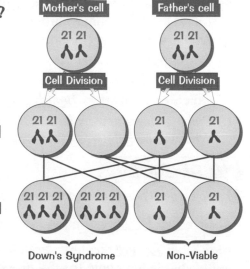

Top Tips:
Three more genetic disorders here, each with their own particular points to be learnt. Remember, two recessive alleles are needed for someone to *suffer* from sickle cell anaemia, but the *carriers* are *protected* from malaria. The important thing about Huntington's Chorea is that it's caused by a *dominant* allele. Down's Syndrome is caused by having *one extra* chromosome. Don't forget to learn the *symptoms* of each disease.

Selective Breeding

Artificial Selection

1) Use the following words to *complete* the blanks:

alleles	breed	characteristics	colours	ears
milk	people	selective	variety	varieties

Artificial selection is when _____ choose what characteristics to breed into living things. This can be used to produce new _____ and breeds of organisms. We choose the individuals which have _____ which are useful to us. We then _____ from these individuals. We choose individuals from the offspring which have the features useful to us, and breed from them. We repeat this over and over again. This is called _____ breeding. A use for selective breeding in agriculture is the production of varieties of plants and breeds of animals that produce greater yields or other desired characteristics. Examples of selective breeding in animals include the Fresian cow that produces greater _____ yields and dogs like the Basset hound that has droopy _____. Plants like wheat have been bred to grow bigger 'ears' with more grain. Also, new varieties of roses now exist with a wide range of flower _____ and shapes. Selective breeding, though, greatly reduces the number of _____ in a population (the gene pool) and therefore reduces _____.

Dog Breeding

2) *People have produced new breeds of dogs to achieve either a particular look or temperament in the dog. Some of the features we have bred in dogs, though, are not advantageous to the dog.*

Shar-pei   Basset hound   Bedlington   Bulldog

a) All dogs have been bred from *wolf* ancestors. Give *two features* of wolves that are no longer found in some modern breeds of dogs.

b) Why are mongrels (random crossbreeds) *healthier* than pedigree dogs?

c) *Some features bred into dogs are not only of no advantage to the dog, they are* *harmful* *to their well being (the price we pay for beauty!). Suggest features of the dog breeds above which could lead to* *health problems* *in the dogs.*

d) *Bulldogs have narrow hips. Often, these dogs can only give birth if they are assisted by people. What would* *happen* *to this breed of dog if people* *stopped assisting them* *to give birth?*

Pig Breeding

3) *The Large White is one of the most common breeds of pig that is kept by farmers in this country.*

a) Give *two features* of a pig that a farmer may be looking for?

b) i) What *feature* has been bred into the Large White pig?
   ii) What is the *name* for the *process* of breeding for specific features?

c) How does the modern breed of pig *differ* from the original wild pig?

d) What is a major *disadvantage* in breeding an animal just for increased yields?

Wild Boar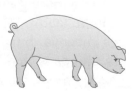

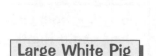 Large White Pig

Selective Breeding

Crossbreeding Wheat

4) People in the Middle East were the first to use wheat for bread making. This is because wheat grew as a wild plant in this area.

   a) i) How did people *improve the quality* of wheat over the last 10,000 years?

     ii) What is the *name* of the process where people select characteristics to *breed* into new plants?

   b) Over thousands of years, rural communities developed the practice of eating the smaller seeds from their crops and keeping the larger ones to sow next year's crop.

     i) Why is this an *example* of selective breeding?

     ii) Name a plant feature *not already mentioned* that has been bred into plants.

Wild wheat | Modern wheat

Black Sea — Georgia

Mediterranean Sea

Arabian dessert

Persian Gulf

Red sea

■ = Areas where wild wheat grew

5) A variety of different plants have been bred from one single plant, the Brassica ancestor.

The diagram shows the variety of plants that have been produced.

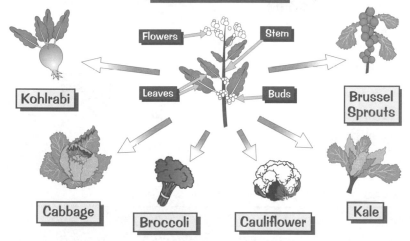

Brassica Ancestor

Flowers | Stem | Leaves | Buds

Kohlrabi | Brussel Sprouts | Cabbage | Broccoli | Cauliflower | Kale

   a) What *part* of the Brassica ancestor has been *selected* for development to produce the:

     i) Cabbage plant?
     ii) Broccoli plant?
     iii) Kale plant?
     iv) Brussel sprouts plant?

   b) Why have plant breeders chosen to produce a *range of plants* from one plant?

   c) *Kohlrabi* has a turnip-like edible stem. What *feature* has been enhanced to develop this plant? Describe the *steps* you could take to *develop* this plant from the Brassica ancestor. What is the name of this *process*?

Selective Breeding Summary

6) Choose the correct word from inside the brackets to *complete* the sentence.

a) The process where people breed animals with the best characterisitcs is *called (artificial / natural)* selection.

b) Selective breeding *(increases / decreases)* the number of alleles in a population.

c) Farmers often selectively breed to *(decrease / increase)* yields of food produced.

d) Selective breeding involves *(asexual / sexual)* reproduction.

e) Breeding characteristics like floppy ears into dogs is *(advantageous / disadvantageous)* to the dog.

Top Tips: This is when people *select* the characteristics they want to breed into plants and animals — it's very useful. You'll need to know *examples* of plants and animals that have been selectively bred. Don't forget the *disadvantages*, too.

Cloning

Tissue Culturing

1) This country exports date palms to Iran and oil palms to Malaysia. The reason we can do this is because Britain has advanced technology in tissue culturing. The diagram shows how tissue culturing works.

   a) What type of _reproduction_ is this?

   b) i) Why are all the plants produced _identical_?
      ii) What name is given to _identical_ offspring?

   c) i) What are the _advantages_ of using tissue cultures?
      ii) What are the _disadvantages_ of using tissue cultures?

   d) What _other_ technique produces identical plants?

Tissue Culturing

Carrot Plant

Cells

Plant out

Cells on sterile growing substance containing hormones

Plant Reproduction from Cuttings

2) When we grow parts of plants into new plants, we call these cuttings.

   a) What _type_ of reproduction is demonstrated here?

   b) How do the plants on the right of the diagram _compare genetically_ with the plants that the cuttings were taken from?

   c) How do seeds from these plants compare genetically with the _parent_ plants?

   d) i) What is the _advantage_ of taking cuttings?
      ii) What is the _disadvantage_ of taking cuttings?

African Violet grown from a single leaf — Leaf

Piece of root — Dandelion plant grown from part of the root

Piece of shoot — Geranium plant grown from part of a shoot

Cloning Techniques

3) Choose the correct word from inside the brackets to complete the sentences.

   a) Plants produced from cuttings grow into new plants by (_meiotic_ / _mitotic_) cell division.
   b) Tissue cultures are a useful way of producing large numbers of (_different_ / _identical_) plants from a small number of cells.
   c) Genetically identical plants are produced by (_asexual_ / _sexual_) reproduction.
   d) Growing plants from tissue cultures (_decreases_ / _increases_) the gene pool.
   e) Cloning techniques are also used in producing identical animals by splitting embryo cells (_after_ / _before_) they specialise.

Types of Reproduction

4) _Place a tick_ in the correct box to show which statements are true of clones.

	CLONES			CLONES	
	YES	NO		YES	NO
Sexual reproduction in strawberry plants			Plants grown from cuttings		
Asexual reproduction in strawberry plants			Plants grown from seeds		
Plants grown from tissue cultures			Identical twins		
An amoeba splitting in two			Non-identical twins		

Cloning

Cloning of Plants

5) Use the following words to *complete* the blanks.

asexual	cells	cuttings	embryo	genetically	host
identical	mitosis	naturally	splitting	tissue	

Clones are _____ identical organisms. These are produced in plants during
_____ reproduction when _____ takes place. In plants, examples include
reproduction by bulbs, stem tubers and runners, as well as _____. Using
_____ cultures also results in genetically _____ offspring, plants
or clones. This technique involves growing new plants from small groups of _____
from part of a plant. Cloning techniques are also used in producing identical cells in agriculture.
This is done by _____ embryo cells (before they become specialised) from a developing
animal _____ and then transplanting the identical embryos into a _____
mother. Clones are also produced _____ as in the case of identical twins.

Cloning of Animals

6) *The diagram shows how animal clones, like cattle, are produced in agriculture. (This isn't how the famous Dolly the sheep was produced, by the way)*

a) By what *process* does the fertilised egg divide?

b) Why are the two offspring produced called *clones*?

c) i) What are the *advantages* of using this technique?
   ii) What are the *disadvantages* of using this technique?

d) *A farmer has a sheep with an excellent coat for making wool. The farmer wants to increase the number of sheep like this he has.*
   i) Would you advise him to use *breeding* or *cloning* techniques?
   ii) Give a *reason* for your answer.

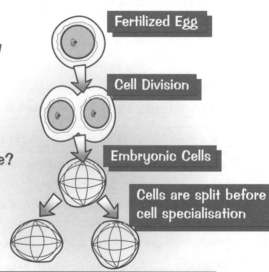

Fertilized Egg

Cell Division

Embryonic Cells

Cells are split before cell specialisation

Two developing embryos transplanted into host mother to produce clones

Cloning Definitions

7) *Match* the definition with the correct word.

cell division which produces identical cells

genetically identical individuals

reproduction which produces variation in plants

reproduction which produces identical plants

cell division producing variation in daughter cells

sexual

clones

asexual

mitosis

meiosis

Top Tips: A scary sci-fi topic if ever I saw one... Relax, clones are just *genetically identical* organisms. You need to be able to describe how *plants* are cloned naturally *and* artificially. Also, learn the diagram of *animal* cloning in question 6. Don't forget the advantages and disadvantages of producing crops and livestock that are clones.

Fossils

Identifying Fossils

1) Use the following words to *complete* the blanks (words may be used more than once).

| animals | decay | fossils | hard | minerals | oxygen | rocks | shells |

Fossils are the "remains" of plants or _____ from many years ago which are found in _____. Fossils are formed in different ways. Most _____ are formed from _____ parts of animals which do not _____ easily. Hard parts include bones, teeth and _____. These parts are eventually replaced by _____ as they decay. The original part retains its structure in the form of rock-like substances. Some fossils are formed from the parts of living things that have not decayed. This is because one or more of the conditions for _____ are absent. In order for decay to occur, _____, moisture, warmth and non-acidic conditions are needed.

Evolution in the Fossil Record

2) *If we study different rock layers, we can see how the same organism changes over a period of time.*

   a) What is the name for these *changes* that occur in living things?

   b) Which is usually the *oldest layer* of rock?

   c) What *two things* can we find out from fossils in rock?

   d) Why are *rocky cliffs* good places to find fossils?

Phacops (trilobite)

Onnia (trilobite)

Olenellus (trilobite)

Preservation without Petrification

3) Petrification (being replaced by rock) is only one way that some traces of life can be preserved.

   a) *Peat Bog Man is an intact body of a man who lived in this country thousands of years ago. The dead body was found in peat. Peat Bog Man was preserved and did not decay. Give a reason why the body did not decay.*

   b) *Insects have been fossilised in tree gum which has solidified into amber. Why did these insects not decay?*

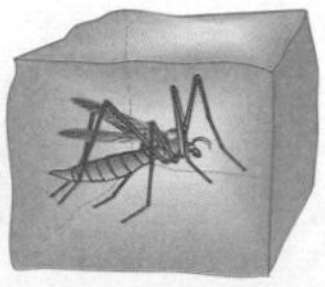

   c) *Some intact, fossilised mammoths have been found in glaciers. These animals are so well preserved that people in Siberia have been known to dig them out of ice and cook their meat for food. Why are mammoths preserved in ice?*

Displaced Fossils

4) *The diagram on the right shows different layers of rock at the top of a mountain.*

   a) Why is the fossil of the fish found at *two different positions* in the rocks on the mountain top?

   b) How is it that fish fossils can be found at the *tops* of mountains?

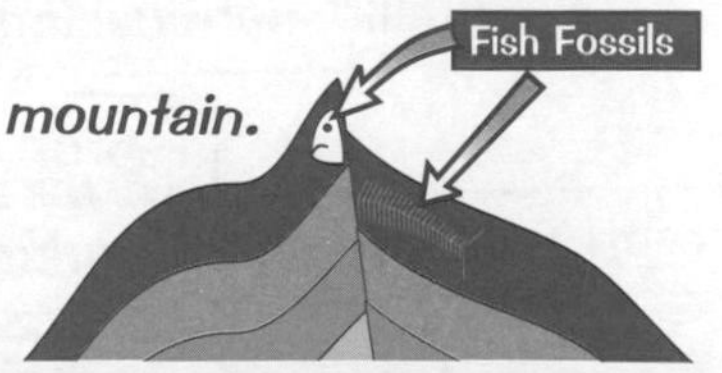

Fish Fossils

5) *Complete* the boxes on the right of the table.

Type of Fossilisation	Reason why dead organism fossilised in this way
Hard parts of animals	
Petrification of soft parts of plants and animals	
Whole organism preserved	

115

Fossils

Places Where Fossils can be Found

6) Fossils in good condition are very rarely found in rocks other than of sedimentary origin.
   a) Common places where fossils are found are quarries, rocky beaches
      and where rocks are cut for road building.
      Give a _reason_ why these are _good places_ to find fossils.
   b) Fossils of sea creatures can be found in rocks at the top
      of mountains. _Explain_ how this happens.
   c) Most of the fossils found are those of sea animals. _Why_ is this?
   d) Most fossils of sea animals only show the shell. The soft
      parts of the animal are not present. _Explain_ why this is.
   e) Many of the plants and animals that are fossilised no
      longer exist. How do we know these are not rocks that
      resemble living things in shape?

Shell Fossil

Same animal before being fossilised

How Fossils are Formed

7) The diagrams below show the four stages that an animal with a shell would undergo to
   become fossilised.

   a) _Complete_ the flow diagram to show how a shell fish is fossilised.

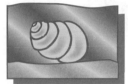

| Shelled animal dies and falls to the bottom of the _____ **1** | shell is covered with _____ **2** | _____ replace the calcite in the shell **3** | Shell turns to _____ (petrification) **4** |

   b) i) Why is the _soft body_ of the shell fish animal not fossilised?
      ii) Why is the _hard shell_ so well fossilised?
   c) What _conditions_ must be _present_ if fossils are to be formed?
   d) Preserved organisms have been found in peat, ice and amber. The absence of which _element_ has
      contributed to their preservation?

8) Coal comes from fossilised trees that have been buried and preserved. Normally when trees die,
   they decay and release their minerals back into the ground.
   a) Why did some trees _not decay_, but become fossilised as coal instead?
   b) How do we _know_ that coal is fossilised wood?

Fossilisation Summary

9) Choose the _correct word_ or _words_ from inside the brackets to complete the sentences.

   a) In order for decay to occur, oxygen (_is_ / _is not_) needed.
   b) Most fossils occur from hard parts of animals because they decay (_quickly_ / _slowly_).
   c) The best fossilisation occurs (_under the sea_ / _on land_).
   d) The (_higher_ / _lower_) in a rock sequence a fossil is found, where the sequence has not
      undergone any movement, the older it is.

Top Tips: Fossils give us great evidence about what prehistoric creatures looked like and how long ago they lived. Remember, there are _three_ ways that an organism can be fossilised — and _three_ ways that the _whole_ organism can be preserved.

SECTION FIVE — GENETICS AND EVOLUTION

Evolution

An Example of Evolution in Horses

1) *The horse evolved to its present appearance over millions of years.*

   a) What <u>*habitat changes*</u> occurred during the period the horse evolved?

   b) *The original horse was no longer than a dog. It lived mainly in marshy, wooded land.*

     i) *Originally, the horse's teeth appeared flat with no ridges.* What does this suggest about the <u>*type of food*</u> they ate?

     ii) *This early "horse" also had <u>many toes</u> to walk on.* Suggest how this helped the horse in its <u>*original habitat*</u>.

     iii) How do we know what the <u>*plant life*</u> was like when this animal was around?

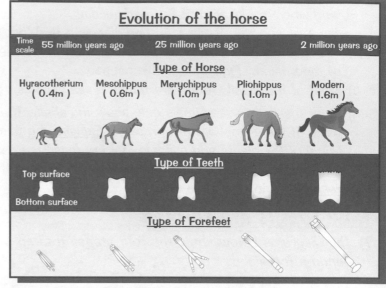

   c) *The modern horse is adapted to living in dry, grassy plains. The plains are open and expose the animal to predators. This means that the horse has to be able to see further afield. Also it needs to be able to run faster if it is to escape predators and survive.*

     i) How did the <u>*body*</u> of the animal change to help it <u>*see further*</u> afield?

     ii) How did the modern horse's <u>*forefeet adapt*</u> to help it <u>*run faster*</u>?

     iii) *Grasses in the plains are hard to chew and wear down teeth.* How did the modern horse's teeth <u>*evolve*</u> to cope with their change in diet?

Explaining how Evolution Works

2) Use the following words to <u>*complete*</u> the blanks.

adaptations	characteristics	changed	Darwin	degenerate	environment	food
evolution	existence	extinct	fittest	nature	organisms	survival	natural

Evolution is about how living things have _____ over millions of years. Lamarck and _____ had different ideas about how this happened. Lamarck believed that new structures appeared when there was a need for them and those that are not used _____. He also proposed that changes acquired in the lifetime of organisms were then passed on to the offspring. Darwin on the other hand proposed that organisms with the best _____ to their _____ survive and have offspring which inherit those adaptations. Useful characteristics become more common. Less well adapted organisms die out — become _____. All _____ over reproduce, so individual organisms have to compete, particularly for _____. Disease and predation cause large numbers of organisms to die. This is called the struggle for _____. This struggle leads to the _____ surviving. In other words, those individuals with the most suitable _____ are the most likely to survive. So, _____ selects the characteristics that are going to aid _____. This is called _____ selection. These gradual changes are the mechanism by which _____ occurs.

Evolution

How Giraffes have Evolved

3) *Place the sentences* in order to explain the evolution of the giraffe.
   - *mutation* resulted in some giraffes having longer necks than others.
   - *all* giraffes had *short* necks.
   - *natural selection* resulted in longer necked offspring surviving.
   - the giraffe population had individuals whose necks *varied* in length.
   - only *long* necked giraffes *survived* the competition for food.

The Evolution of Vertebrates

4) The diagram shows the earliest occurrence and abundance of fossil vertebrates.

a) What were the *first vertebrates* to evolve?
b) The dinosaurs became extinct about 60 million years ago. What *evidence* is there of this in the diagram?
c) Which were the *last vertebrates* to evolve?
d) How do fossils help us to *understand* evolution?
e) Although the diagram shows evolution as being continuous, there are many missing links in the fossil record of many animals. How can we *explain* these missing links?

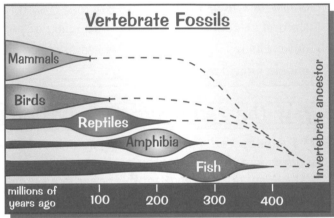

Vertebrate Fossils

Mammals

Birds

Reptiles

Amphibia

Fish

Invertebrate ancestor

millions of years ago 100 200 300 400

The Evolution Of Man

5) *A number of different ideas exist about the evolution of man. The diagram shows one possibility of what may have happened. One of our closest animal relatives, the chimp, had a common ancestor with man. This common ancestor lived about 5 million years ago. Even today, 98% of human DNA is also found in chimps.*

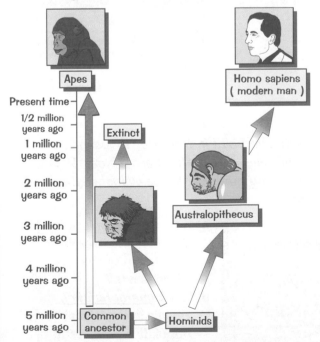

Apes

Homo sapiens (modern man)

Present time
1/2 million years ago
Extinct
1 million years ago
2 million years ago
Australopithecus
3 million years ago
4 million years ago
5 million years ago Common ancestor → Hominids

a) i) *The split from the common ancestor produced different species. What does* species mean?
   ii) *All human groups today belong to the same species. How do we account for the* physical differences *in the different races?*

b) What must have happened in the bodies of the *common ancestor* to produce different species?

c) *About 6 million years ago there was a change in the plant life where the common ancestor lived. Tropical rainforests declined and were replaced by scrubland (with small shrubs), small woods and vast areas of grassland called Savannah. It is around this time that our ancestors split from the chimp ancestor. Our ancestors left the woods and became upright animals.*
Why did we end up becoming *taller and walking on two limbs?*

Top Tips: Evolution is how living things *gradually* change over *millions of years* — think about the horse, and how natural selection shaped its evolution.

Natural Selection

Survival of the Fittest

1) Use the following words to *complete* the blanks.

alleles	disease		environment		favourable		offspring
natural	die	species		survive		variation	

There is a wide range of _____ within particular _____ because of differences in their genes. Predation, _____ and competition (often for food) cause large numbers of individuals to _____. Individuals that survive are those that are most suited to their _____. Those individuals that survive pass on their genes (and therefore their characteristics) to their _____. This process is known as _____ selection. Natural selection can alter the frequency of particular _____ in a population. Alleles determining _____ characteristics increase in frequency. This is because alleles which enable individuals to _____ are passed on to the next generation.

How the Peppered Moth has Adapted

2) *The peppered moth is normally light in colour. Occasionally, a black variety appears. Insect eating birds like the thrush prey on these moths.*
   a) i) How does a *black* moth appear in a population of *light* coloured moths?
      ii) How is the population of these moths kept *constant*?

   b) *In 1848 the first black variety was noticed in Manchester. By 1895, 98% of the moth population of Manchester was black. During this time, the environment also became darker as a result of increasing pollution.* Why did the number of black moths *increase so dramatically* between 1848 and 1895?

   c) *Today, in industrialised areas, the population of dark moths is almost 100%. In Scotland and South-West England the reverse is true.* Why does this *happen*?

   d) Why is the black variety *not* a new species?
   e) What is the name for the *process* that determines the survival features of a population?

Peppered Moth

White and Black peppered moths on tree bark in unpolluted area

White and Black peppered moths on tree bark in polluted area

Migration and its Effects

3) *The Wildebeeste is a large antelope-like animal. At a particular point in the year, thousands of Wildebeeste start on a migration, walking for hundreds of miles across Southern Africa. When slowing down to cross rivers, hundreds of animals are killed by hunters. Some Wildebeeste die of exhaustion, while others are crippled or killed by predators.*

   a) How can this migration be *good* for the overall population of the Wildebeeste?
   b) What *characteristics remain* in the Wildebeeste population as a result of this migratory run?
   c) How is *natural selection* demonstrated here?

SECTION FIVE — GENETICS AND EVOLUTION

Natural Selection

Controls on Population Sizes

4) In every generation, the numbers of plant and animal offspring produced greatly outnumbers the parent's population. In spite of this, the tendency is for the numbers of living things to remain constant.

a) Why do the <u>number</u> of plants and animals remain fairly <u>constant</u>?

b) *The table shows how human populations have increased over a period of time.* Why has the human population <u>increased</u> in this way when most animal populations stay constant?

Time	Population Size
12,000 years ago	4 million
2,000 years ago	170 million
1820	1,000 million
1930	2,000 million
1960	3,000 million
1974	4,000 million
1987	5,000 million
1997	6,000 million

c) In 1859, twelve pairs of rabbits from Britain were taken to a ranch in Australia, where there was an abundance of grass and large open spaces. Australia has few natural predators.

i) Use the information in the graph to explain what happened to the <u>number</u> of rabbits.
ii) Give <u>three reasons</u> why the population changed in this way.

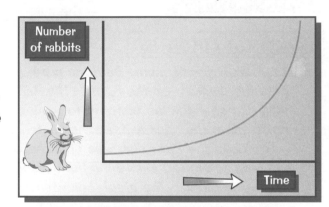

d) *Eventually, the rabbit population was brought down by infecting the rabbits with the disease myxomatosis.* What would <u>eventually</u> have happened to the <u>population</u> of rabbits if they were not infected in this way? <u>Explain</u> your answer.

e) *Even though the whole population was exposed to myxomatosis, some rabbits survived.*
i) <u>Why</u> did this happen?
ii) How is the <u>present</u> population of rabbits in Australia <u>different</u> from the original population that was introduced there in 1859?

The Process of Natural Selection

5) <u>Complete</u> the sentences by choosing the correct words from inside the brackets.

a) The frequency of alleles which determine useful characteristics (<u>decreases</u> / <u>increases</u>) in a population.
b) Factors like disease cause a population to (<u>decrease</u> / <u>increase</u>).
c) Organisms that are the best survivors are those that are (<u>best suited to their environment</u> / <u>strongest</u>).
d) Survivors pass their genes on to their (<u>offspring</u> / <u>partner</u>).
e) Natural selection is the process by which (<u>evolution</u> / <u>mutation</u>) takes place.
f) In order for changes to occur in the characteristics of a population, (<u>mutation</u> / <u>predation</u>) must take place.

Top Tips: Natural selection — top theory. The <u>environment</u> selects characteristics that make individuals <u>survivors</u>. Survivors can <u>pass on</u> their <u>genes</u> to their children, who then pass them on to theirs — that's how evolution <u>works</u>. The natural world is very harsh, and even a <u>small competitive edge</u> makes a <u>big difference</u>. The story of the Peppered Moth is an example of evolution through natural selection that happened recently.

Population Sizes

Habitats and Environments

1) *There are twelve sycamore trees in a wood. Their environment is quite sunny, with plenty of nutrients in the soil. They share the wood with many other plants and animals.*
   a) What is the <u>population</u> of sycamore trees?
   b) What is the <u>habitat</u> of the sycamore trees?
   c) What is the <u>community</u> in the wood?
   d) <u>Match</u> the terms to the correct definitions:

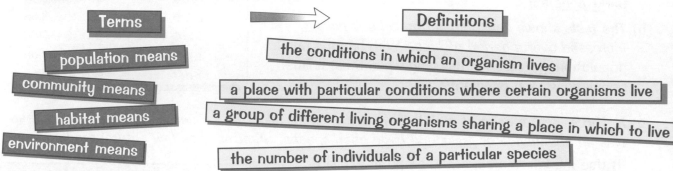

Terms	Definitions
population means	the conditions in which an organism lives
community means	a place with particular conditions where certain organisms live
habitat means	a group of different living organisms sharing a place in which to live
environment means	the number of individuals of a particular species

Bacteria Colonies

2) *In an experiment, some bacteria were grown in a Petri dish (see the diagram on the right). The Petri dish had a layer of jelly-like agar for the bacteria to grow on and there were nutrients in the agar to feed the bacteria. Over the course of a few days the Petri dish was checked, and the number of bacteria estimated each time by measuring the size of the bacterial colony. The graph below shows the results obtained.*

colony of bacteria

Petri dish with agar

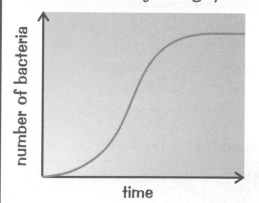

a) Is the Petri dish the bacteria's <u>habitat</u> or <u>environment</u>?
b) What do we call the <u>number</u> of bacteria in the dish?
c) Describe the <u>shape</u> of the graph. What happens to the rate of increase in bacteria during the experiment?
d) Why does the number of bacteria only increase <u>slowly</u> at first?
e) *The number of bacteria reaches a maximum near the end of the experiment. Suggest why the number of bacteria <u>does not</u> just keep on going up. Mention <u>two factors</u> in your answer.*

3) *In another experiment, two different species of bacteria, **A** and **B**, were grown in Petri dishes. Graph 1 shows the results when they were grown separately, and graph 2 shows what happens when they were grown together on the same Petri dish.*

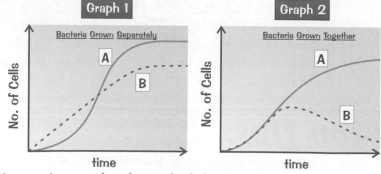

a) What word is used to describe the <u>two species</u> of bacteria growing together on the same Petri dish?

b) Explain why one species of bacteria <u>almost dies</u> out by the end of the second experiment, but the other continues to grow in number. (<u>Hint</u> : Look carefully at graph 1)

Population Sizes

Animal Populations

4) The cane toad was brought to Australia in 1935. It grows up to 24cm long, and can lay up to 40,000 eggs in one season. It is highly poisonous to other animals, and most native tadpoles cannot live in the same water as cane toad tadpoles. The map on the right shows how far it has spread — and it is still on the march.
Suggest reasons why the cane toad _has been so successful_ in Australia.

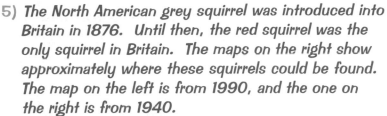

5) The North American grey squirrel was introduced into Britain in 1876. Until then, the red squirrel was the only squirrel in Britain. The maps on the right show approximately where these squirrels could be found. The map on the left is from 1990, and the one on the right is from 1940.

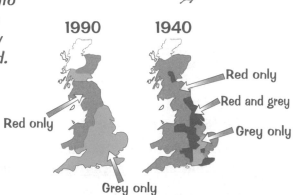

1990   1940

Red only
Red and grey
Grey only
Red only
Grey only

   a) _Describe the changes_ in the distribution of the squirrels.
   b) Suggest _reasons_ for these changes.

Predators and Prey

6) The graph on the right shows the change in the numbers of a species of predator and its prey over time.
   a) What do the words _predator_ and _prey_ mean? Give _two examples_ of a predator and its prey.
   b) What do you notice about the changes in the numbers of predator and prey with time? _Explain_ why these changes happen.

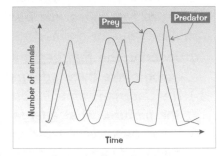

7) The number of mice in a wood was estimated at the same time each year for thirteen years. The results obtained are shown in the chart on the right.

   a) _A road was built through the middle of the wood at the end of year 8. What _effect_ has this had on the _number of mice_ in the wood? What _effect_ will this road have on the study _in future years_?
   b) Suggest _two reasons_ why the number of mice in the wood fell between years 4 and 5 of the study.
   c) Suggest _two reasons_ why the number of mice in the wood rose between years 6 and 7 of the study.
      (Don't just write down the opposite of your answers to part b).

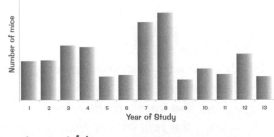

8) _Draw a table_ with the headings shown on the right. In the "factor" column list the things that can affect the size of a population of organisms. In the "examples" _give an example_ of this factor at work. (Try to think of plant examples as well as animal examples.) One line has been done for you as an example.

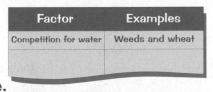

Factor	Examples
Competition for water	Weeds and wheat

Top Tips: Population size is an odd thing to study. It's actually just _common sense_ if you remember that organisms _thrive_ if: they've got the _things they need_ (water, light, food, etc); they're _better_ at getting those things than the _competition_; they don't get _eaten_ and they don't get _ill_. Remember that, and it won't get too complicated. Don't forget, you need to know, and _explain_, why predator and prey populations go in _cycles_.

Communities (Adapt and Survive)

Desert Animals

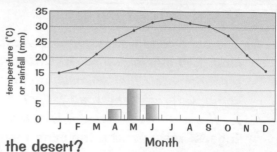

1) The graph on the right shows the average daytime temperature (line) and rainfall (bars) on the northern edge of the Sahara desert. Although it can be over 57°C in the day, at night the temperature can fall below 0°C. Sometimes it does not rain for years.

   a) *From this information*, what is the environment like in the desert?

   b) You possibly thought that the desert is just lots of sand. Just 15% of the Sahara desert is covered by sand dunes, the rest is stone plateaus or gravel surfaces. What *problems* will animals and plants living in a desert face? What will happen to them if they are *not adapted* to the desert?

2) The Sidewinder is a snake which lives in deserts. It moves sideways across the sand by throwing its body into a series of S-shapes, always keeping a loop of the S-shape off the ground, with two other parts touching. *Explain why* it does this?

3) Many desert animals, such as the kangaroo rat, spend the day in a burrow and come out at night. What are the *advantages* and *disadvantages* of doing this?

4) Camels are probably the best-known animals in the desert. There are two types, the Bactrian camel (right) and the Arabian camel or dromedary (left).

   a) Describe the *features* that the camels have in common which make them *adapted* for desert conditions.

   b) The Bactrian camel is found in high rocky deserts where it gets very cold in winter. From the picture, what *adaptation* does the Bactrian camel have to allow it to survive there?

   c) It has been discovered that a shaved camel loses nearly twice as much body water as an unshaved camel. Suggest *why* losing its hair could cause this *difference*.

   d) Humans need to maintain a fairly constant body temperature, but camels can tolerate a big change in their body temperature. They can allow it to go from about 34°C to 41°C during the day, and then they cool off during the night. This means that during the day they do not need to use methods of cooling that humans do. How is this *advantageous* to the camel?

Desert Plants

5) The following features are adaptations of desert plants to allow them to survive the environment.

   a) The seeds of flowering desert plants can lie dormant in the soil for years until the rain allows them to germinate, grow, and flower quickly.

   b) Some plants have long roots which reach deep underground.

   c) Some plants have shallow roots which spread just under the surface.

   d) Succulent plants store water in their leaves, stems, and roots.

   e) Some plants drop their leaves during a dry spell. They usually have small leaves.

   f) Some plants take in and store carbon dioxide at night. During the day their stomata are closed.

   g) Many plants have modified leaves which form thorns, and photosynthesis occurs in the stems.

Study each of these features carefully. *For each feature*, decide what *condition* in the environment the plant has adapted to, and explain *how* the adaptation *helps* the plant to survive in the desert.

Communities (Adapt and Survive)

Survival in the Arctic

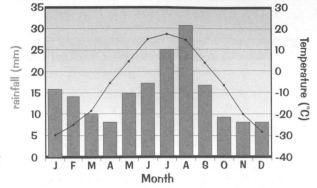

6) The graph on the right shows the average daytime temperature (line) and rainfall (bars) in the Arctic. The temperature can fall to -80°C and the wind can blow at over 300 km/h. In the winter, it is dark all the time, but in the summer the sun shines all the time.

a) From this information what is the *environment* like in the Arctic?

b) It's not all sea-ice in the Arctic. There is a lot of barren land too, known as the tundra. The plants there often grow very close to the ground, and have small leaves. *Suggest why* the plants grow like this.

c) What *problems* will animals face living in the Arctic? Suggest some adaptations that would allow animals to live successfully in the Arctic.

d) It is warm enough in the summer for mosquitoes. What other *problems* will this cause?

7) Look at the two cubes on the right. Cube 1 has sides 1cm long, and cube 2 has sides 2cm long.

a) Calculate the *volume* in cm³ of each cube. Calculate the *surface area* of each cube (remember — a cube has six sides!). Finally, calculate the *surface area* to *volume ratio* for each cube (divide the surface areas by the volumes). Which cube has the *greatest* surface area to volume ratio?

b) Animals with a large surface area to volume ratio lose heat more quickly than those with a small surface area to volume ratio. In general, what sort of animal will *lose heat* most quickly? *Explain* your answer.

Life in the Arctic Circle

8) Lemmings are small rodents that live in the tundra. They have a rounded body about 12cm long. Their fur is light brown, and they have small ears that are hidden by fur. Lemmings live in burrows. *Explain* how the lemming is *adapted to life* in the Arctic.

9) Polar bears and walruses are probably the best known animals in the Arctic. Both have large bodies, with thick layers of fat under the skin. The polar bear has fur that looks white in the light. The walrus has long tusks and tough brown skin. Male walruses often fight each other.

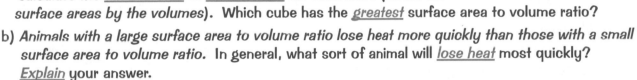

a) Suggest *why* polar bears and walruses do not live in burrows.

b) Explain how polar bears and walruses are *adapted* to life in the Arctic.

10) The snowshoe hare has white fur in the winter and reddish-brown fur in the summer. Suggest a *reason* for this change.

11) Desert foxes have very large ears, whereas Arctic foxes only have very small ears. Suggest a *reason* for this difference (*it is not to do with hearing or hiding*).

12) Where there are predators there must be prey. The whole animal kingdom revolves around this system.

a) Design the *ultimate predator*. Explain *how* it is adapted to be successful at catching prey.

b) Design the *ultimate prey*. Not an easy prey, but prey that is *very difficult* for a predator to catch or eat. Explain *how* it is adapted to escape from predators.

Top Tips:
Obviously, animals and plants *not* suited to the environment will be *less likely* to survive than those which *are*. By *natural selection* (remember), creatures have evolved *features* that help them to cope. Learn all the camel/desert and polar bear/arctic features — they're *shared* by lots of other animals in *similar environments*, so don't panic if it isn't a polar bear or a camel that you get in the Exam. Remember the ways that plants adapt, too.

SECTION SIX — THE ENVIRONMENT

Atmospheric Pollution

The Composition of the Atmosphere

1)

Pie chart label	Name of gas	Approx. % in air
A	'others'	21
B	argon	0.07
C	carbon dioxide	78
D	nitrogen	0.04
E	oxygen	0.9

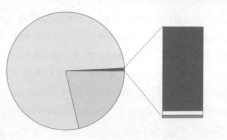

a) The table above is muddled up, *copy it* putting everything into the correct place.

b) *Atmospheric pollution involves adding more carbon dioxide and additional gases to the "others". What do you notice about the amounts of these gases in the atmosphere?*

Burning Fossil Fuels

2) *When fossil fuels burn, the carbon in them reacts with oxygen to form carbon dioxide.*

a) What does "*fossil fuel*" mean? Give *three examples* of a fossil fuel.

b) What happens to the amount of *carbon dioxide* in the atmosphere when fossil fuels are burnt?

c) *When fossil fuels are burnt, some of the carbon does not react completely with oxygen, and particles of black carbon are produced. This is called soot. What problems will this soot cause to plants if it settles on the leaves?*

d) *Most fossil fuel contains small amounts of sulphur.* Which *gas* will be produced when sulphur reacts with oxygen during burning?

e) *The gas named in part d) causes breathing difficulties. In which areas and at what time of year are people most likely to suffer breathing difficulties due to this gas? Which groups of people are most likely to be at risk from this gas?*

Ozone

3) *Ozone (not "o-zone") is a gas with the chemical formula O_3. Ordinary oxygen, O_2, can be converted into ozone by passing electric sparks through it. Ozone has a strong smell, and it can often be smelt near electrical equipment such as photocopiers and laser printers.*

a) *During and just after thunderstorms, there is often a sharp smell in the air. What is likely to have caused this smell?*

b) *The Victorians thought that ozone was good for them. They also thought that there was a lot of ozone at the seaside, and started the idea of taking holidays by the sea, especially if they were recovering from an illness. Can you suggest why they might have thought that ozone was good for them? (Look at its chemical formula.) Why might they have thought that there was a lot of ozone at the seaside?*

c) *Ozone is a health hazard. It can cause breathing problems and stinging eyes. However, it can be used to purify water and to sterilise air. Why do manufacturers usually advise that photocopiers and laser printers should only be used in well-ventilated rooms?*

d) *Ozone can also be produced when sunlight shines on exhaust fumes from cars. Where and when would you expect ozone to cause the greatest hazards to health? Suggest what could be done to reduce the amount of ground-level ozone in the air.*

e) *Ozone can cause the breakdown of chlorophyll. What problems would this cause?*

Atmospheric Pollution

Ultraviolet light

4) The Sun provides us with heat and light. In addition to the light we can see, the Sun also produces ultraviolet light (UV light).

   a) Ultraviolet light can damage proteins. Why do people who _work outside_ in the Mediterranean often have darkened skin and lots of wrinkles?

   b) Ultraviolet light can also damage the DNA in the nucleus of the cell. What are the likely _dangers_ to pale-skinned Europeans of sunbathing a lot?

   c) Why should you wear _sunglasses_ when you are outside in the sunlight?

CFCs and the Ozone Layer

5) Ozone created at ground level by human activity is dangerous, but at 25 - 50 km above us, ozone reaches its maximum natural concentration of 10 parts per million. This is the ozone layer, which absorbs ultraviolet light from the Sun.

   a) Suggest _how_ this ozone layer formed naturally.

   b) _Explain_ why the ozone layer is important to plants and animals.

Chlorofluorocarbons (CFCs) are compounds that only contain chlorine, fluorine and carbon. CFCs have no smell, and do not dissolve in water. They are non-toxic, very unreactive chemicals with low boiling points. They have been used in refrigerators, aerosol sprays and in expanded polystyrene food containers.

   c) _Why_ are CFCs used in expanded polystyrene food containers and fire extinguishers?

   d) CFCs do not easily break down into other chemicals in the environment. _Suggest why_.

Until recently, the amount of ozone in the ozone layer has stayed the same because new ozone was being made at the same rate as it was being broken down by chemicals found naturally in the atmosphere. However, when ultraviolet light is absorbed by CFCs, it causes them to turn into highly reactive chemicals that can turn ozone into oxygen.

   e) What _effect_ will CFCs have on the ozone layer, and how do they get there?

   f) The Montreal Protocol is an international agreement to stop making most CFCs and to use alternative "ozone-friendly" gases instead. This has already started to happen, but the ozone layer will continue to be affected for many years to come. _Why_?

Lead Poisoning

6) A compound called tetraethyl lead is added to 4-star leaded petrol to make it burn more evenly in car engines. Lead is called a _cumulative poison_ because once it gets into the body, it is difficult for the excretory system to remove it. Lead causes damage to the nervous system including the brain.

   a) _Where_ is lead poisoning most likely to be a problem?

   b) Suggest how the _amount of lead_ polluting the atmosphere could be _reduced_.

   c) Steps have been taken to reduce the amount of lead in the air, and the amount of lead detected in children at risk is coming down. _Why_ are people still suffering lead related problems?

7) _Draw a table_ with the headings shown on the right. In the "_pollutant_" column, write down the names of the major air pollutants you have studied. In the "_problems_" column, write down the _problems_ caused to living things by these pollutants, and in the "_remedies_" column write down possible ways in which the pollutant could be tackled and _reduced_.

pollutant	problems	remedies

Top Tips: This is all rather depressing, really. What you need to do (apart from becoming an eco-warrior) is make sure you've got damage to the _ozone layer_ separate in your mind from the _greenhouse effect_ and global warming. Take care, because it can be confusing. You need to know _where_ the pollutants come from and _what damage_ they do.

SECTION SIX — THE ENVIRONMENT

The Greenhouse Effect

The Moon and the Earth

1) The temperature on the surface of the Moon ranges from -175°C to 125°C, with an average temperature of about -20°C.

   a) _Where_ does the Moon get its _heat energy_ from? What would happen to any _water_ on the surface of the Moon?

   b) The average distance of the Moon from the Sun is the same as the Earth's average distance from the Sun. From this information, what _temperature_ would you expect on the Earth's surface?

   c) The temperature on the surface of the Earth actually ranges from ⁻89°C to 58°C, with an average of 14°C. _Compare_ the temperatures of the Earth with those of the Moon.

   d) The difference between the temperature on the surface of the Moon and that on the Earth is due to the _greenhouse effect_. _Copy_ and _complete_ the sentences below about the greenhouse effect, choosing the correct words from the underlined pairs:

   "Energy from the _Moon_ / _Sun_ passes through the Earth's _atmosphere_ / _surface_ and _cools_ / _warms_ the Earth's surface. Heat energy from the Earth's surface is radiated into _space_ / _the ground_ but some of it is _absorbed_ / _reflected_ by gases in the atmosphere. This _cools_ / _warms_ the atmosphere, which is _good_ / _bad_ for life on Earth. However, excess CO_2 / O_2 produced by burning fossil fuels is causing the earth to warm up too much which may cause flooding and drought."

Greenhouse Gases

2) Only some of the gases in the atmosphere, called _greenhouse gases_, are good at absorbing heat energy. These include carbon dioxide and methane, which both occur naturally in the atmosphere.

   a) Name a _natural source_ of carbon dioxide.

   b) Since the Industrial Revolution began in the 19ᵗʰ century, humans have been burning fossil fuels.
   Name a greenhouse gas _released_ by _burning fossil fuels_.

   c) Study the _top graph_ on the right, which shows the amount of carbon released from burning fossil fuels since 1850. _Describe_ the graph — how has the release of carbon from fossil fuels _changed_? Suggest _why_ this change happened.

   d) Study the _bottom graph_ on the right, which shows the amount of carbon dioxide in the atmosphere since 1850. _Describe_ the graph — how has the amount of carbon dioxide in the atmosphere _changed_? Suggest _why_ this change happened.

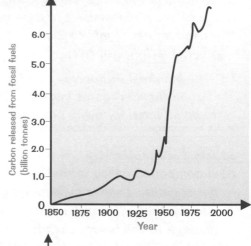

   e) Work out approximately how many times _more_ carbon was released in 1975 compared to 1875.

   f) Work out approximately how many times _more_ carbon dioxide there was in the atmosphere in 1975 compared with 1875.

   g) _Compare_ your answers to parts **e)** and **f)**. Can you tell if all the _carbon_ released from fossil fuels has ended up as _carbon dioxide_ in the atmosphere? Explain your answer.

   h) There are natural processes that can absorb the carbon released as carbon dioxide from fossil fuels. _Name_ one of these processes.

   i) Explain what the _changes_ in the amount of carbon dioxide in the atmosphere could do to the temperature of the Earth.

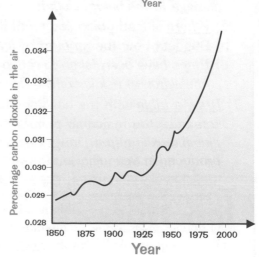

SECTION SIX — THE ENVIRONMENT

The Greenhouse Effect

Temperature Rises and CO_2

3) *The two graphs on the right show the changes in the amount of carbon dioxide in the atmosphere since 1850, and the changes in average global temperature per year in °C since 1880.*

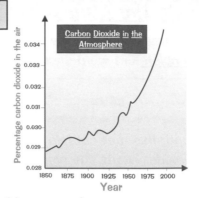

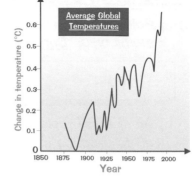

   a) <u>*Describe the changes*</u> in average temperature.

   b) <u>*Discuss*</u> the extent to which it is possible to say that the temperature changes are caused by the changes in the amount of carbon dioxide in the atmosphere.

The graph to the right shows the changes in sea level. <u>Compare</u> this graph with the one showing changes in temperature.

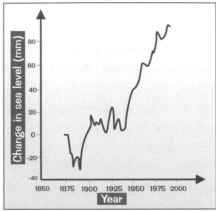

   c) Suggest <u>*how*</u> changes in the Earth's temperature ("global warming") could cause a <u>*change in sea level*</u>.

   d) Explain what you think <u>*might happen*</u> if the amount of carbon dioxide in the atmosphere continues to rise. Make sure you consider the possible effect on <u>*low-lying*</u> areas of the world.

The Effects of Worldwide Farming

4) *Carbon dioxide is not the only greenhouse gas — methane is also very important. Natural gas is mostly methane, but cattle also produce it as a result of their digestive processes. Two other important sources of methane are rice paddy fields, and rotting vegetation that has been submerged by rising water when dams for hydroelectric power are built.*

The graph on the right shows the ten countries that produced the most greenhouse gases in 1991. Many Third World countries are becoming industrialised to increase their wealth. As people become wealthier, they tend to eat more meat and to use more fossil fuels. In many countries, land for cattle is obtained by cutting down and burning forests.

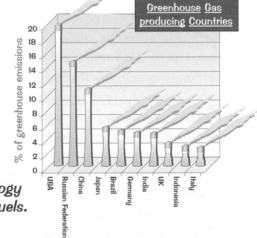

   a) How does farming <u>*contribute*</u> to the greenhouse effect?

   b) Explain the <u>*influence*</u> of increasing industrialisation and wealth on the <u>*production*</u> of greenhouse gases?

   c) *Hydroelectric power, HEP, is regarded as a "green" technology because it does not involve burning non-renewable fossil fuels. Is HEP as "green" as people think?*

5) *In a study using computer models, it was found that a doubling of atmospheric <u>carbon dioxide</u> and global warming (producing <u>warmer</u> and <u>wetter</u> weather) would double the amount of wood produced in Scandinavia. Suggest why trees would <u>grow better</u> in such conditions.*

Top Tips: You've got to understand the <u>*factors*</u> that lead to an increased greenhouse effect and global warming. Remember — <u>*natural*</u> things also produce greenhouse gases (look at question 4). The greenhouse effect itself is good for life on Earth because it keeps us nice and warm, but getting <u>*too*</u> warm will muck up the <u>*climate*</u> and melt the <u>*ice caps*</u> — and totally <u>*drown*</u> whole countries. Don't mix up the ozone layer with the greenhouse effect, will you.

Acid Rain

Releasing Sulphur into the Atmosphere

1) a) Petrol and diesel contain hydrocarbons. These compounds consist of carbon and hydrogen atoms only. _Copy and complete_ this word equation to complete the combustion of these fuels.

FUEL + ... ⟹ .... + WATER

b) Most fossil fuels have impurities that contain sulphur. The sulphur reacts with oxygen in the air to produce sulphur dioxide. Write the _word equation_ for this reaction.

c) In car engines, the temperature can become so high that nitrogen in the air reacts with oxygen to produce nitrogen oxides. Write the _word equation_ for this reaction.

d) Some of the petrol does not burn completely, and carbon monoxide and unburnt hydrocarbons pass out of the exhaust. _List the chemicals_ that are likely to come out of the exhaust _(assume that a catalytic converter is not present)._

The Acidity of Rainwater

2) If an oxide of a non-metal dissolves in water, it makes an acid. For example, carbon dioxide dissolves in water to make carbonic acid. Clouds contain water vapour. When the water vapour cools, it condenses to form water droplets that join together and fall as rain.

a) Suggest _two sources_ of carbon dioxide (one natural and one man-made). Explain _why_ rainwater is _naturally_ slightly acidic.

b) The chart shows the solubility of several substances in water. Which substances are most soluble in water?

c) Will the gases in your answer to part **b)** produce acids? _Explain_ your answer, and _name_ any acids that you think will be formed.

d) _Explain_ how cars might cause acid rain (_your answers to question 1) will help_).

3) Katie tested some rainwater samples with universal indicator solution to find out how acidic they were. She matched the colours on a chart to work out their pH numbers.

a) Rainwater sample A was pH6, sample B was pH2, and sample C was pH4. _Which sample_ was probably _uncontaminated_ rain? _Which_ was the _most_ acidic? _Explain_ your answers.

b) Katie next tested some laboratory acids. They were all at the same concentration. Nitric acid and sulphuric acid were both pH 1, and carbonic acid was pH 4. What do these results tell you about these acids?

c) Katie diluted the nitric acid and sulphuric acid with a lot of distilled water, and tested them again. She now found that they both had a pH of 3. What _effect_ does diluting acids have on their _pH_ and _level_ of acidity?

d) Suggest conditions which would cause _very acidic rainwater_ to form.

4) The table on the right shows the approximate contribution of different sources of acid rain gases in the UK.

a) Show these results as a suitable _graph_ or _chart_.

b) Which of the gases is present in the greatest amount?

c) Which source produces the most sulphur dioxide, SO_2?

d) Which source produces the most nitrogen oxides, NO_x?

e) Which source contributes the most acid rain gases?

Pollutant	Source	%
SO_2	Industry	10
	Other	8
	Domestic	5
	Power stations	34
NO_x	Road transport	22
	Power stations	13
	Other	5
	Industry	4

SECTION SIX — THE ENVIRONMENT

Acid Rain

Damage Caused by Acid Rain

Amount of
damage
☐ Little
▨ Some
▰ A lot

5) *Acid rain can react with limestone and marble statues and stonework on buildings, causing them to be eroded. For a long time, it was not clear that acid rain was damaging trees. The map on the right shows how much damage has been done to trees in Europe. The circles show how much acid rain pollution there is, starting with the most in the centre, and becoming less further out.*

    a) Discuss how much the evidence in the map *supports* the idea that acid rain damages trees.

    b) *Britain, Germany and France produce a lot of acid rain gases, but the Scandinavian countries in the north do not. Suggest why Scandinavia has quite high levels of acid rain and damaged trees.*

6) *Research has shown that acid rain can damage trees, especially conifers like spruce and pine, causing their leaves to fall off. It also reacts with minerals in the ground, such as aluminium, magnesium and potassium, causing them to dissolve and be washed away underground.*

    a) Suggest *what will happen* to a tree that loses some of its leaves due to acid rain.

    b) *Aluminium is toxic to trees, but is usually insoluble. Explain how acid rain could poison trees.*

    c) *Magnesium is found in chlorophyll.* What would you *expect* to happen to plants growing in areas where acid rain is falling? *Explain* your answer.

    d) *The roots of trees in acid soils can grow poorly.* What *effects* will this have on these trees?

    e) Draw a *diagram* to summarise the effects of acid rain on trees.

The Danger to Rivers and Lakes

7) *As acid rain falls into rivers and lakes, they become increasingly acidic. Water flowing off the land contains high levels of aluminium and mercury released by the acid rain.*

    a) What will happen to the water plants in acidified lakes and rivers?

    b) *Small crustaceans at the bottom of the aquatic food chain die if the pH falls below about 6.* What will happen eventually to the other animals in the lake if the pH falls *below 6*?

    c) *The soluble aluminium can react with sulphuric acid to make aluminium sulphate. This clogs the gills of fish with sticky mucus.* Suggest the *likely effect* of this on the fish.

    d) *In some parts of Europe, fish caught from acidified lakes are condemned as unfit for human consumption. Suggest a reason for this.*

8) *A lot of money is now being spent to combat acid rain because of its economic effects as well as its environmental costs.* Suggest *three* economic effects of acid rain.

9) *There are two main ways to combat acid rain. First, the acid in the environment can be neutralised. For example, powdered lime (calcium oxide) can be added to lakes and soils. This reacts with the acids and raises the pH closer to 7. The lakes have to be treated regularly, however. Secondly, the release of acid gases at source can be avoided. For example, the "flue gases" coming out of power stations can be treated with limestone (calcium carbonate). This reacts with sulphur dioxide and produces gypsum (calcium sulphate). This can be used in plasterboard and for filling in quarries.*

    a) Why do lakes have to be treated *more than once*? What *problems* does this treatment cause?

    b) What are the *advantages* and *disadvantages* of treating the flue gases as described above?

Top Tips:
There are two key bits here — the causes and the effects of acid rain. You'll need to know where the two main acid rain gases come from and the acids they form (be prepared to give a *word equation*). You really should know *at least two* effects of acid rain. Watch out for questions that bring in ideas of changing population size and things happening *further up the food chain* as a result of acid rain contamination.

Farming and its Problems

Population Growth

1) *Three hundred years ago, there were about 600 million people in the world, 40 years ago about 2.5 billion, and about 6 billion now. In 1798, Thomas Malthus predicted that increases in food production would not keep up with human population growth, and that there would be famine.*

   a) What do you notice about the <u>increase</u> in the population over the last three hundred years?
   b) *There are indeed famines but, taken overall, enough food is produced to feed everyone adequately. <u>Suggest why</u> people still starve when there is enough food to go around.*
   c) *The list below shows some of the things that have allowed modern farming to keep up with the growth in population. For each one, <u>explain how</u> it has helped <u>increase</u> food production.*

   | Artificial fertilisers | Artificially selected animals and plants | Mechanisation |

Modern Farming Techniques

2) *More use of machinery (mechanisation) has caused the average size of fields and farms to increase greatly. This has been achieved by felling trees and removing hedges between smaller fields.*
   a) Why are <u>larger fields</u> needed for machinery such as combine harvesters, tractors and ploughs?
   b) <u>What problems</u> are caused to wildlife communities when trees and hedges are removed?

3) *In some parts of the world, large areas of forests have been cut down to make way for farms.*
   a) What problems might cause some countries to remove large areas of forest in order to provide more farmland?
   b) *Photosynthesis causes carbon dioxide to be removed from the atmosphere and to be locked up as wood.* What will happen to the <u>uptake</u> of carbon dioxide from the atmosphere in deforested areas? What will happen to the <u>production</u> of oxygen in these areas?
   c) *Frequently, trees are burnt after being cut down, producing carbon dioxide.* How will your answers to part b) <u>affect the impact</u> of doing this?
   d) *Trees that are not burnt may be allowed to decay by the action of microbes.* Explain how this will contribute to the release of <u>carbon dioxide</u> into the atmosphere.
   e) *Trees transport water from the ground to their leaves where it evaporates.* What is this <u>process</u> called? What will happen to the <u>amount</u> of <u>water vapour</u> in the atmosphere if trees are removed? What effect could this have on the <u>rainfall</u> in the deforested region?
   f) *Roots bind the soil together.* When it rains, what will happen to the <u>soil</u> in places where trees have been removed? What is this <u>process</u> called? Why might this lead to <u>flooding</u>?

Soil Quality Issues

4) *When crops are harvested, they contain minerals obtained from the soil.*
   a) Explain what will happen if these minerals are <u>not replaced</u>.
   b) *Organic fertilisers, e.g. compost, contain minerals and humus.* <u>Name</u> another organic fertiliser.
   c) *Artificial fertilisers contain minerals but no humus. Humus improves the texture of the soil, allowing it to hold water and to release minerals gradually.* What are the <u>advantages</u> of using artificial fertilisers? Suggest a <u>disadvantage</u> of using them.

5) *Pesticides are chemicals that include insecticides, herbicides and fungicides.* What do each of these <u>pesticides</u> do? *Sometimes, these chemicals kill other organisms in addition to the pests.* <u>Suggest</u> some <u>environmental consequences</u> of this happening.

Farming and its Problems

Eutrophication

6) The sentences below are steps in a lake becoming eutrophic, but they are muddled up.
   a) Sort them into the _correct order_ and _write them down_.

- Fish and other aquatic animals die of suffocation.
- The microbes take more oxygen from the water for their respiration.
- Excess fertilisers leach from the soil and are washed into the lake.
- The number of microbes that feed on dead organisms increases.
- There is increased competition between the plants, and some die as a result.
- Water plants in the lake start to grow rapidly.

b) In the corrected sequence, _why should_ water plants grow more quickly?

c) What _resources_ are the water plants _competing for_? Which resource is probably in excess?

d) If there are more plants in the lake, you might expect more oxygen to be produced by photosynthesis. _Why_ does the oxygen content of the water _go down_ instead?

Normally, the action of decomposers such as bacteria is welcomed because it allows scarce nutrients to be recycled for use by other organisms in the community, as in the nitrogen cycle.

e) Why is the action of decomposers such a _problem_ in the case of a eutrophic lake?

f) Describe some environmental and economic _consequences_ of eutrophication.

g) Suggest _two courses of action_ that might be taken to rescue a lake which is becoming eutrophic.

Man-Made Problems

7) Untreated sewage has the same effect as dead vegetation in the process of eutrophication.
   a) What part does raw sewage play in eutrophication?
   b) In many parts of the world, the discharge of raw sewage is increasing. _Why_ is this happening?
   c) In addition to eutrophication, what other _hazards_ are there in discharging sewage into lakes, rivers and seas?

8) Many timber-producing areas are some distance from the nearest road. Logs are towed over a river or lake to the sawmills. Some get stuck, become waterlogged and then sink. _Describe_ what might happen to a lake as a result.

9) a) What is a _pesticide_? Give an _example_ of a pesticide. Why are pesticides useful to farmers?
   b) In a study of an aquatic food chain in a small pond, it was found that many of the animals contained a fat-soluble pesticide called Kilzemall. The results are shown below. _Describe_, and _explain_, the trend in the concentration of Kilzemall going up the food chain.

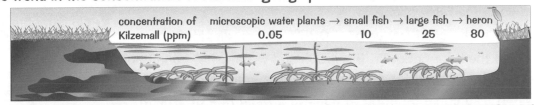

concentration of Kilzemall (ppm)   microscopic water plants → small fish → large fish → heron
0.05   10   25   80

   c) Kilzemall was designed to kill insects in wheat fields and not insects in water. _Suggest how_ the pesticide got into the pond.
   d) In later studies, scientists were astonished to discover that polar bears and penguins contained high amounts of Kilzemall in their bodies. _Suggest how_ the pesticide managed to get into their bodies. Remember: polar bears and penguins only meet in zoos, and farmers are not likely to be doing any farming at the poles.
   e) Modern pesticides are tested in many ways to ensure their safety.
   Explain _why_ we should be concerned about the health of organisms exposed to pesticides.

Top Tips: This topic boils down to _three_ themes: fertilisers, pesticides and deforestation. You need to understand how _each_ of these damages the environment. Remember that _eutrophication_ is what happens when water plants grow _far too quickly_ and have to compete and use up all of the resources. Don't muddle up _fertilisers_ and _pesticides_ — they cause harm in very different ways. Sadly, all this is the price we pay for cheap, plentiful food.

Managed Ecosystems

Vegetation and Land Use

1) *The pie-chart on the right shows the main categories of the Earth's plant production. The degraded land includes built-up areas, derelict land and damaged land that can no longer support crops. The unused productive land is land that could be grazed by animals or used for timber and food, but is wasted.*

a) What *percentage* of the Earth's plant production do humans use to provide food and timber?

b) *Suggest how* we could feed more people without interfering with uncultivated wild land.

c) How might these figures *change* in the future? *Give reasons* for your answers.

Efficient Food Production

2) *Modern farming often involves monoculture.*

a) What is *monoculture*? What are the *benefits* of growing crops in this way? What are the possible *drawbacks*?

b) *If crop plants are sown too close together, yields may begin to fall. Suggest a reason* why.

c) *In some areas, sheep or deer are farmed rather than food crops. What sort of area might* not be suitable *for crops, but could still support grazing animals?*

3) *Intensive farming methods have been developed to maximise food production while reducing labour and land usage. Although pig and poultry farms take up very little land themselves, the land they* actually require *is much larger. Why is this?*

4) *The graph on the right shows how the growth rate of a variety of tomato plant changes with increasing temperature.*

a) At what *temperature* does this plant grow fastest?

b) What factors are likely to be *limiting* the growth rate at this temperature?

c) *Explain* why the rate of growth falls at high temperatures. *In a separate experiment, the effect of changing the concentration of carbon dioxide was studied. The results are shown in the table below.*

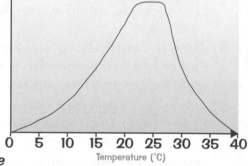

d) What is the *significance* of 0.035% carbon dioxide?

e) From the information in the graph and table, what conditions might be *optimal* for growing tomatoes commercially?

Concentration of CO_2 (%)	Relative rate of growth
0.035	0.45
0.35	1.00

f) What else could be done to achieve a *rapid rate* of growth?

g) *Commercial growers often grow their tomatoes in greenhouses.* Explain the *benefits* of growing crops in a greenhouse, *compared* to growing them outside in fields.

Fish Farming

5) *Fish farming has become increasingly popular, especially with expensive species of fish. To be successful, the farmer must ensure that the fish are safe from predators, fed the correct diet, and kept free of disease. Chemicals are usually used to protect the fish from parasites such as lice.*

a) Why is fish farming mostly used for *expensive* fish such as trout and salmon?

b) How can the farmer keep the fish *safe* from predators?

c) What would happen if the fish were fed *too little* food?

d) What would happen if they were fed *too much*?

e) Suggest a possible *danger* in using chemicals for this purpose.

Managed Ecosystems

Insect Control

6) The information on the right is taken from the packet containing a natural predator of aphids. The predator is an insect that can protect a number of plants in greenhouses from aphids.

Aphid control needed	Number needed per metre	Frequency of treatment	Number of treatments
To prevent aphid infestation	1 to 3	Monthly	continue
To control light infestation	2 to 5	every two weeks	3
To control moderate infestation	4 to 8	every two weeks	4
To control heavy infestation	7 to 12	every two weeks	5
To maintain control	1 or 2	every three weeks	continue
Notes		Predators are cannibals - keep them well separated.	

a) As the severity of the aphid infestation increases, what happens to the _treatments_ needed? _Suggest why_ the treatments need to be changed in this way.

b) Vince wants to control a moderate infestation of aphids in his greenhouse. What _treatments_ will be necessary to bring the aphids under control? What other _precautions_ could be taken? What would be the benefit to Vince if he had _prevented infestation_ in the first place?

c) Why does the predator have to be released _regularly_ just to maintain control?

d) As it was a lot of hard work just to kill some insects, Vince decided to spray them with _Kilzemall_ (a chemical insecticide). From the information given, suggest some _problems_ with this biological pest control. What _problems_ and _benefits_ might there be in using _Kilzemall_ instead?

Pest Control

7) Rabbits were introduced into Australia and quickly became widespread pests. Native animals and plants have suffered declining populations and soil erosion has increased.

a) i) Suggest why rabbits were so _successful_ in Australia.
   ii) Why should rabbits affect the _populations_ of native animals and plants?
   iii) Why has _soil erosion_ increased?
   iv) What might be the _effect_ on farm animals where there is a large rabbit population?

The first attempt to control rabbits in Australia was at the end of the 19th century, when 300 cats were released. A lot of the cats starved, and the rabbit population was not affected.

b) Suggest why the cats were _not able_ to control the rabbit population.

In the 1950's, myxomatosis (a disease caused by a virus) killed nearly 99% of the rabbits. The numbers of rabbits has increased since, and the virus now kills less than 50% of the rabbits.

c) Explain why the virus killed _most_ of the rabbits in the 1950s, but much _fewer_ today.

A virus that causes another disease, rabbit calicivirus disease (RCD), was released in Australia in 1996. It kills up to 90% of the rabbits, and has spread through most of the rabbit population.

d) What measures should be taken _before releasing_ such a virus?

e) Where RCD is found in rabbit populations, wildlife authorities control the populations of predators such as dingoes and cats. _Explain why_ predators need to be controlled.

f) When farmers have released the RCD virus, they have been advised to destroy rabbit warrens and shoot rabbits. _Why_ should they do this when the virus kills up to 90% of the rabbits?

g) _Explain_ what might happen to the rabbit population of Australia in a few years time.

Non-Native Plants

8) Many countries have imported water hyacinth from South America as a decorative plant. In some places, however, it has "escaped" into local waterways. It has tough stems and big leaves, and it grows quickly, overtaking native plants. A weevil has been found that eats its stems and leaves.

a) Suggest some _problems_ that lots of water hyacinths might cause in rivers and lakes.

b) Suggest a _suitable plan_ to tackle water hyacinth in an infested lake. You should _take into account_ that its seeds also grow quickly, and can still germinate after 17 years in the mud.

Top Tips: Managed ecosystems, like _fish farms_ or _greenhouses_, are cool. You can _protect_ your crop from pests with chemical or biological control, control the _conditions_, and (slightly tricky one, this) _maximise_ the _energy transfer_ up the food chain. It's possible to produce food _and_ maintain a balanced ecosystem by using organic fertilisers, set-aside and biological pest control.

Foodwebs

Basic Terminology

1) a) _Match_ the terms to the correct definitions:

terms	definitions

Carnivores are

Herbivores are

Consumers are

Producers are

Omnivores are

organisms that can make their own food, e.g. by photosynthesis

animals that eat other animals

animals that can eat both plants and other animals

animals that eat plants

organisms that rely on other organisms for their food

b) Give an _example_ of a herbivore, a carnivore and an omnivore.

Food Chains

2) A → B → C is a food chain.
   a) What does it tell us about the _organisms_ A, B and C? What do the _arrows_ mean?
   b) What _type_ of organism would you expect A to be? Why?
   c) In the food chain, grass → cow, _identify_ the consumer and the producer.
      Why does the arrow point _from_ the grass to the cow, and _not_ the other way around?

3) _Constructing food chains._
   a) Construct a _food chain_ using the following organisms: blue tit, caterpillar, hawk, oak tree.
   b) _Explain_ what is meant by the terms _primary consumer_, _secondary consumer_, and _tertiary consumer_. _Refer_ to the food chain in part **a**) in your answer.

Woodland Foodweb

4) _Study_ this woodland foodweb. It shows all the woodland food chains interconnected.
   a) Write down the _food chains_ involved in this food web (there are seven).
   b) _Identify_ the primary, secondary and tertiary consumers in the woodland.
   c) Which animal has the _greatest_ range of foods?
   d) Which animals eat two _different_ foods?
   e) _There are three organisms that are not eaten by anything. What are _they_?
      What general _name_ is given to such organisms?
   f) _Explain why_ foodwebs are usually more useful than food chains.

Marine Foodweb

5) _Study_ the information below about life in the sea.

   · Phytoplankton are tiny algae that can carry out photosynthesis.
   · Zooplankton are tiny crustaceans, jelly fish and molluscs that eat phytoplankton.
   · Zooplankton are eaten by fish, penguins and humpback whales.
   · Fish are eaten by seals, penguins and humpback whales.
   · Seals and penguins are eaten by killer whales.

   a) Write down all the _possible_ food chains from the information given (_there are five_).
   b) Use your _food chains_ to construct a foodweb. It usually helps to put the producer at the bottom, then gradually work upwards to the top carnivores.
   c) What are the _top carnivores_ in this food web?

SECTION SIX — THE ENVIRONMENT

Foodwebs

Trophic Levels

6) a) What is meant by "*trophic level*"?
b) Using the woodland foodweb on the right, *identify* the organisms found in the first, second, third and fourth trophic levels.
c) In which *trophic levels* are producers, herbivores and carnivores found?
d) *One of the organisms in the community is an omnivore. Which one is it, and how can you tell?*
e) *The hawk flies into an electricity line and is killed.* Explain what will eventually happen to the *numbers* of great tits in the wood.
f) What *effect* will the hawk's death eventually have on the number of stoats in the community?
g) *Some mink escape from a farm and find the mice especially tasty. Explain* what will happen to the number of mice in the wood as a result of the mink escaping.
h) What *effect*, if any, will there be on the number of stoats as a result of mink eating mice?
i) *The mink also manage to catch, and eat, the great tits.* What *effect*, if any, will there be on the number of stoats as a result of this new information?

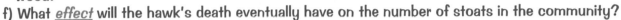

7) *Dead organisms are a source of food in communities, too.* What *name* is given to organisms that break down dead animal and plant material? Give *two examples* of such organisms.

Shallow Marine Foodweb

8) *The food web below shows some of the organisms found on the Grand Banks off the coast of Newfoundland. The Grand Banks have been an important fishing ground.*

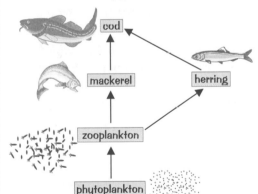

a) Copy the *foodweb*, leaving space for more organisms and lines.
b) *Eels eat zooplankton, and are eaten by cod. Add* this information to your foodweb.
c) *When zooplankton die, they sink to the seabed where sandworms and crabs eat them. Add* this information to your web.
d) *Haddock eat sandworms, and are eaten by cod. Cod also eat crabs.* Add this information to your foodweb.
e) What roles do the *phytoplankton* and the *cod* have in this foodweb?
f) From the information given, *which organisms* eat living zooplankton?
g) What is the *importance* of the organisms named in part f) to the cod?
h) What is the *importance* of crabs and sandworms to the cod?
i) *Some trawlers damage the seabed and the creatures living there.* Suggest a possible *consequence* for the fish on the Grand Banks of this sort of damage.
j) *One important consumer is missing from the food web — people. Herring, mackerel, haddock and cod have been over-fished and the fishing ground is now exhausted.* Why has the number of people *not decreased* as a result of over-fishing? What organisms are likely to remain in *large* numbers?

Top Tips: There are pretty pictures to be looked at here, but the really important thing is to learn what the words mean and understand *what eats what*. Don't draw arrows the wrong way or you'll get dangerous cow-eating grass. You'll be asked to work out what will *happen* if an organism is added to, or taken away from, the food web. Some of these questions can be a bit *tricky*, so think through all the steps *carefully*.

Pyramids of Number and Biomass

Understanding the Structure of Pyramids

1) *The blank pyramid below could be a pyramid of numbers or a pyramid of biomass.* <u>Copy</u> *the diagram.*
   On the <u>left-hand side</u> *of your diagram,* <u>label</u> *the arrows to show which step refers to the primary,*
   secondary and tertiary consumers (the producer has already been labelled for you). On the <u>right-hand side</u> *of your diagram,* <u>label</u> *the arrows to show which trophic level each step refers to.*

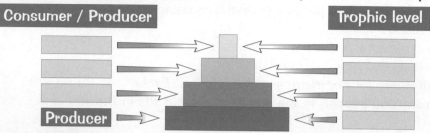

Food Chain Pyramids

2) <u>Draw</u> pyramids of numbers for the following food chains. <u>Make sure</u> you label each step with the name of the organism and how many of them there are.

   a) | microscopic water plants (1 million) → water fleas (100,000) → trout (50) → kingfisher (1) |

   b) | oak tree (1) → caterpillars (500) → birds (5) |

   c) Ideally, the width of each bar would be drawn to scale, so that the trout bar in part **a)** would be fifty times wider than the kingfisher bar. This is usually not possible. <u>Explain why</u>.

   d) If you have done part **b)** correctly, it will not look very pyramid-shaped. <u>Why</u> can a pyramid of numbers have an unusual shape like this?

   e) <u>Draw</u> a pyramid to show the following short food chain: wheat → human. <u>Decide</u> on a suitable width for the wheat bar (thousands of plants might be needed to feed one person). In tropical countries, a disease called schistosomiasis can be a big problem. It is caused by a parasitic worm, about 1cm long, which lives in the blood vessels and feeds on blood. A person might be infected by dozens of these worms. <u>Add</u> a labelled bar to your pyramid of numbers. <u>Explain why</u> this pyramid is not pyramid-shaped.

   f) Think of another food chain that will produce a pyramid of numbers that is <u>not</u> pyramid-shaped. <u>Draw</u> and <u>label</u> the pyramid, and write down the food chain along side it. <u>Explain</u> why your pyramid has its unusual shape.

Number Pyramids

3) Pyramid information:
   a) What <u>information</u> does a pyramid of numbers give?
   b) In the food chain, carrot → rabbit → fox, <u>which row</u> in the table on the right represents the most likely numbers of each organism?
   c) What do you notice about the <u>size</u> of the organism as you look from left to right along this food chain?

	Carrots	Rabbits	Foxes
A	1	100	4000
B	1	4000	100
C	100	1	4000
D	100	4000	1
E	4000	1	100
F	4000	100	1

   d) Which pyramid of numbers below most closely <u>matches</u> the correct answer to part **b)**?

   A
   Fox
   Rabbits
   Carrots

   B
   Fox
   Rabbits
   Carrots

   C
   Carrots
   Rabbits
   Fox

   e) What do you notice about the <u>size</u> of the organism and the <u>width</u> of its bar on the pyramid of numbers in the correct answer to part **d)**?

Pyramids of Number and Biomass

Understanding Mass

4) *Godfrey wanted to find the mass of some grass before giving it to his pet rabbit. He remembered that a lot of the mass in the grass is water, so he decided to find out how much water was in there. He put the grass in his mum's oven, and warmed it. He took the grass out and weighed it at regular intervals. His results are shown in the table.*

Weighing	Mass (g)
1	125
2	64
3	33
4	18
5	11
6	10
7	10

a) *Draw* a suitable graph to show Godfrey's results.

b) Why did the last two weighings give the *same* mass?

c) Work out the *mass* of water in the grass. What *percentage* of the original mass is this?

d) What percentage of the *original mass* of the grass is left at the end of the experiment? What will be in the material that is left?

Biomass Pyramids

5) *Explain* what is meant by the word *biomass*. What *information* does a pyramid of biomass give?

6) *One of the food chains in the North Sea is: phytoplankton → zooplankton → mackerel → cod. The biomass of each of the organisms in the food chain was estimated from samples and experiments. It was found that for every 1kg of cod, there was 100kg of phytoplankton, 80kg of zooplankton and 10kg of mackerel. In each case, the masses are dry masses.*

a) What does dry mass mean? Why does it allow *fairer* comparisons to be made between the biomass of different organisms?

b) *Draw* a pyramid of biomass for this food chain. Draw it *to scale*, and make sure that you label each bar with the name of the organism and its biomass in kg.

c) *In some pyramids of numbers and biomass, the top bar can be shown as a vertical line. Explain* why this is sometimes necessary.

d) Between which two organisms in this food chain is the *most* mass lost? *How much* mass?

e) Between which two organisms in this food chain is the *greatest proportion* of mass lost?

f) Suggest reasons why the biomass is *less* at each trophic level than the one before it.

g) *The wet mass of adult mackerel averages about 1.5kg, and that of adult cod averages about 7.5kg. Assuming that both types of fish have the same proportion of water in their bodies, how many* mackerel feed one cod?

7)

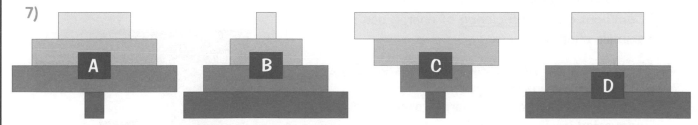

Explain which of the pyramids above could *represent*:

a) The pyramid of numbers for a community that relies on a large producer.

b) The pyramid of biomass for a woodland community.

c) The pyramid of numbers for a food chain that ends with parasites such as fleas.

d) The pyramid of numbers for a marine community in which the producers are tiny algae.

Top Tips: This stuff is pretty easy. Just remember that it takes *a lot* of food from the level below to keep one animal alive. Remember that *pyramids of biomass* always get narrower the higher up you go, but *pyramids of numbers* can be any shape — because you can have a hundred fleas on one dog, but they will still weigh a lot less than the dog. Easy.

Energy Transfer

Photosynthesis

1) *Photosynthesis uses energy to produce the sugars needed for respiration.*

 a) What *type* of organism can photosynthesise? What type of energy is *absorbed* to drive photosynthesis, and from where does it come? Write down the *word equation* for photosynthesis.

 b) *All living organisms respire.* Write down the *word equation* for *respiration*. Energy is *released by respiration.* What is this *energy* used for? Give *more than one* answer.

 c) *Where* did the energy released by respiration originally come from?

2) *The diagram on the right shows what happens to the energy falling on a plant leaf. One transfer of energy is missing; this is the energy used to produce glucose by photosynthesis.*

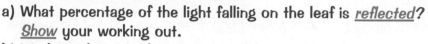

 a) What percentage of the light falling on the leaf is *reflected*? *Show* your working out.

 b) Work out how much energy is used to produce *glucose* by photosynthesis. What percentage of the *light* falling on the leaf is this?

 c) *Plants respire, and for respiration use 20% of the energy used to produce sugars in photosynthesis.* How much *energy* is this? *Show* your working out.

 d) Work out what percentage of the original energy falling onto the leaf is *converted* into new materials, after allowing for the energy used in respiration. Comment on the *efficiency* of plants in harnessing light energy.

Energy Efficiency

3) *The diagram on the right shows what happens to the energy in grass when a sheep eats the grass.*

 a) What percentage of the energy consumed is lost in *wastes*, and what percentage in *respiration*?

 b) *The remaining energy is used to produce new growth in the sheep.* *Work out* how many kJ this is, and the percentage of the original energy consumed. *Show* your working out.

 c) Comment on the *efficiency* of energy use in animals such as sheep.

4) *The chart on the right shows the transfer of energy when a carnivore eats its prey.*

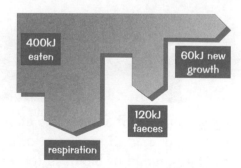

 a) What percentage of the energy taken as food is *converted* into new growth?

 b) What percentage of the energy taken in as food is used in *respiration*?

5) *Energy cannot be created or destroyed but it can be converted from one form to another:*

 a) What *happens* to the energy when an animal eats food?

 b) *Consider* a typical food chain of plant → herbivore → carnivore. What percentage of the energy content is *transferred* from one trophic level to the next in a food chain?

 c) *Using* your answers to questions 2) — 4), starting with 1,000,000kJ of sunlight, how many kJ will end up as *new growth* in the carnivore?

SECTION SIX — THE ENVIRONMENT

Energy Transfer

Energy Losses

6) *The diagram on the right shows the fate of energy,*
   captured by photosynthesis in barley plants,
   as it passes through pigs on its way to humans.

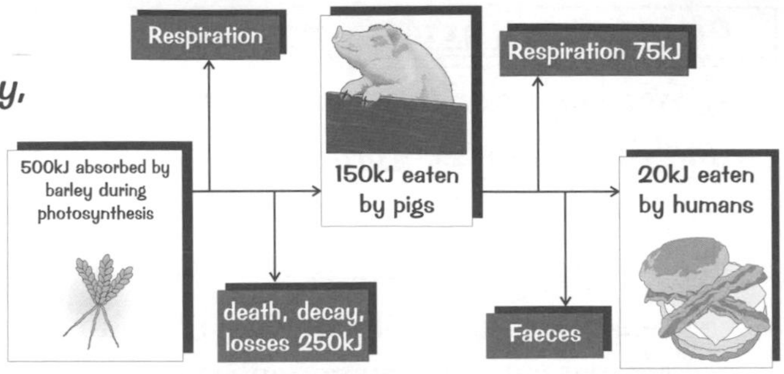

   a) Work out how much energy is *lost* from
      the barley plants by *respiration*.

   b) Work out how much energy is *lost* from
      the pigs in *faeces*.

   c) What *percentage* of the original 500kJ absorbed by the barley is passed to the pigs, and
      how much is passed to the humans? *Show* your working out.

It's difficult to stop the pigs producing faeces, but if the amount of respiration by the pigs could be
reduced, more energy would pass to the humans.

   d) For what *purposes* do the pigs use energy released by respiration?

   e) *Suggest ways* that the amount of respiration by the pigs could be *reduced*, giving reasons
      for your answers.

   f) *More people could be fed if they ate the barley, instead of letting the pigs eat it and then eating*
      the pigs. *Work out* how many times more people might be fed this way.

   g) *Apart from respiration by the barley and the pigs, there are two other sources of energy*
      loss. *What* are they? *Suggest how* the energy lost in these ways could be *reduced*.

Diagram labels: Respiration | Respiration 75kJ | 500kJ absorbed by barley during photosynthesis | 150kJ eaten by pigs | 20kJ eaten by humans | death, decay, losses 250kJ | Faeces

Better Use of Food Energy

7) *It is often suggested that if everyone became a vegetarian, ten times more people in the world could be fed.*

   a) Use your knowledge of energy transfer in food chains *to explain* this idea.

   b) *In practice, fewer extra people would be fed in this way.* Suggest *two reasons* for this.

8) *For each of the following animals, decide whether they use energy from respiration to keep warm*
   ("warm-blooded") or not ("cold-blooded"): amphibian, bird,
   fish, insect, mammal, mollusc, reptile, and spider.

   a) Make a *table* with the headings shown on the right, and put
      the animals in the correct column of the table.

Warm-blooded	Cold-blooded

A typical bird might lose 95% of its energy intake through
respiration and faeces, a mammal 90%, an insect 80%, and a spider 70%.

   b) *Explain* these differences in energy loss. If insects and spiders lose much less energy than
      mammals and birds, why don't we eat lots of locusts and spiders (*people in some parts of the*
      world love them fried)?

   c) *Study* the marine food chain below, together with the biomass of each organism.

   Phytoplankton → zooplankton → fish → dolphin
   400 tonnes   160 tonnes   20 tonnes   1 tonne

   Explain why 1 tonne of dolphin needs 20 tonnes of fish, but 1 tonne of fish only needs 8 tonnes of
   zooplankton (*tiny sea creatures*).

Some scientists believe that they can work out whether dinosaurs were warm-blooded or cold-
blooded by seeing how many carnivore fossils there are compared to herbivore fossils.

   d) *Explain how* this information could be *used* to decide if dinosaurs were warm-blooded or not.

Top Tips:
These pages give you the *reason why* you have biomass pyramids. *Energy,*
originally from the sun, works its way up the food web, and an enormous
90% gets lost at each stage. Remember that energy and material are always lost in the waste
materials of organisms, and energy is lost through *respiration* just by *being alive*. Don't forget that warm-
blooded animals need to eat more food to stay warm.

SECTION SIX — THE ENVIRONMENT

The Carbon Cycle

Plant Photosynthesis and Respiration

1) *Word equations and symbol equations are often the clearest way to write down a concept.*

   a) Write down the <u>word equations</u> for photosynthesis and respiration in plants.
   The substances involved are carbon dioxide, glucose, oxygen and water.

   b) Which process <u>releases</u> energy, and which one <u>needs</u> energy? <u>Where</u> does each process occur?

   c) Which process will <u>release</u> a carbon compound into the atmosphere, and which one will <u>remove</u> carbon compound from the atmosphere? Which carbon compound is <u>involved</u>?

   d) Look at the two processes. <u>Describe</u> the similarities and differences between them.

   e) *The diagram on the right represents part of the carbon cycle. <u>Copy it</u>, and <u>fill in</u> the missing words and process names. Leave plenty of space to add more processes to your diagram.*

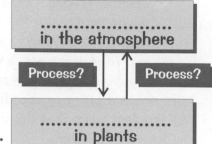

Carbon Compounds

2) *Plants can use the product of photosynthesis to make other compounds that contain carbon. The table shows the chemical formulae of some compounds found in plants.*

   a) What do these compounds have in <u>common</u>?

   b) Which of these substances could be made by a <u>plant</u>?

   c) i) What can be <u>made</u> from fatty acids and glycerol?

   ii) from amino acids?

   d) What is the <u>importance</u> of these substances to animals?

Compound	Formula
amino acid (glycine)	$C_2H_5O_2N$
fatty acid (octadecanoic acid - stearic acid)	$C_{18}H_{36}O_2$
glycerol	$C_3H_8O_3$
carbohydrate (glucose)	$C_6H_{12}O_6$

3) When an animal feeds on a plant, in general what happens to the <u>carbon compounds</u> from the plant? What <u>use</u> does the animal make of them? What happens to the <u>carbon</u> in these compounds when the animal respires? <u>Add</u> to your carbon cycle the processes of feeding and animal respiration.

Destruction of Forests

4) *People are cutting down many forests to make way for their building and farming needs.*

   a) What is the word used to <u>describe</u> cutting down forests?

   b) Give four reasons <u>why</u> people are cutting down forests.

   c) What will happen to the amount of carbon dioxide in the <u>atmosphere</u> as a result of cutting down forests? Use your carbon cycle to <u>help</u> you to explain your answer.

When a forest is being cleared, often the quickest way to remove the fallen trees is to burn them.

   d) Which gas in the air <u>reacts</u> with the wood when it burns, and which gases are produced?

   e) Write the word equation for <u>burning</u> wood in oxygen. <u>Add</u> the process of burning to your carbon cycle. Make sure that your arrow points in the <u>correct</u> direction.

   f) What will happen to the <u>amount</u> of carbon dioxide in the atmosphere when trees are burnt?

5) <u>List</u> the processes discussed on this page that <u>remove</u> carbon dioxide from the atmosphere, and those processes that <u>return</u> carbon dioxide to it. <u>Explain</u> the importance of plants in the carbon cycle. <u>Why</u> is the carbon cycle called a <u>cycle</u>?

The Carbon Cycle

Decomposition and Decay

6) Plant cell walls contain cellulose fibres. Cellulose consists of thousands of glucose molecules joined together. However, the way in which they are joined means that the enzymes in most animals are not able to break down cellulose. Ruminants, like cows, have bacteria in their digestive system that can break down cellulose. Fungi are also able to break down cellulose.

   a) What _substance_ might be formed when cellulose is digested?

   b) What would happen if there were _no_ bacteria and fungi _capable_ of digesting cellulose?

7) Bacteria and fungi can break down solid waste materials from animals. They can also break down materials in dead animals and plants. This is known as decomposition or decay.

   a) What general _word_ is used to describe bacteria and fungi that break down dead material?

   b) What is the _benefit_ to the bacteria and fungi of digesting these materials?

   c) What carbon compound will be _returned_ to the atmosphere as a result of their activities?

   d) What substances will they _release_ into the soil?

   e) Why are bacteria and fungi important for the _recycling_ of carbon in the carbon cycle?

The Role Played by Microbes

8) _Copy_ and _complete_ these sentences about decomposition and decay by microbes. _Choose_ the correct word from each of the _underlined_ pairs.

   "Microbes digest materials faster when they are in _cool_ / _warm_ conditions which are _moist_ / _dry_. Many microbes work better if there is more _oxygen_ / _nitrogen_ in the environment."

9) Humans make use of microbes to treat sewage before discharging it into rivers.

   a) What is sewage? Why should we want to _treat_ it before discharge? Suggest some uses for the materials produced during treatment of sewage.

   b) Suggest _suitable conditions_ for the microbes to break down sewage efficiently.

   Humans also make use of microbes in garden compost heaps.

   c) Why is compost _better suited_ for the garden than the original ingredients?

   d) What sorts of materials are _suitable_ for making compost? What do we use _compost_ for?

Remembering the Carbon Cycle

10) Did you know that the _carbon cycle_ is a _crab cyclone_ if you rearrange the letters? Decay of plant and animal material by fungi and _bacteria (I eat crab)_ is part of the carbon cycle.

   a) _Rearrange_ the underlined words below to find a sentence to do with decay and decomposition. _Come do press_, _ye cad_, _wee gas_. (there are three words, separated by the commas)

   b) What do _Eric Sailboat_ (two words) and _Konrad Web_ (one word) have to do with decay?

11) Describe the journey made by a _carbon atom_, beginning as carbon dioxide in the atmosphere, becoming part of a fossil fuel such as oil, and being returned to the atmosphere by burning. Mention the _names_ of the processes involved at each stage.

Top Tips: The Carbon Cycle — another beautiful example of _nature's intrinsic harmony_, and another _diagram_ for you to learn. Remember that there's only _one_ way that carbon dioxide gets from the atmosphere into the general plant and animal biomass, and that's photosynthesis. The plants and animals then get _eaten_ or turned into _useful stuff_. Finally they either get _burnt_ or they _rot_, releasing carbon dioxide back into the atmosphere. Don't forget about decomposition — they like asking you how to make _good compost_, so just make sure you know.

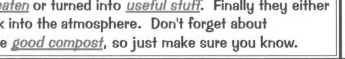

SECTION SIX — THE ENVIRONMENT

The Nitrogen Cycle

Atmospheric Nitrogen

1) The majority of the Earth's atmosphere is nitrogen.

a) What is the approximate *percentage* of nitrogen gas in the atmosphere?

b) *Ammonia can be manufactured from nitrogen and hydrogen using the Haber Process. The ammonia is then converted into nitrates for fertilisers. The Haber Process needs temperatures of about 450°C, pressures of about 200 atmospheres and an iron catalyst.* What does this information tell you about the *reactivity* of nitrogen?

c) *Plants and animals cannot use nitrogen from the atmosphere to make new substances directly.* Suggest a reason *why*.

> *In thunderstorms, lightning provides enough energy to react nitrogen from the air with oxygen (a similar process takes place in a hot car engine).*

d) What *mixture of gases* will be *produced* as a result of this reaction?

e) When these gases dissolve in rainwater, which acid will be *produced*?

f) When the acidified rain soaks into the soil, the acid reacts with minerals to produce nitrates. However, only very little nitrate is made as a result of lightning compared to other processes. Suggest a reason *why*.

g) The diagram on the right represents part of the nitrogen cycle. *Copy it*, filling in the missing words. Leave plenty of space to add more processes to your diagram.

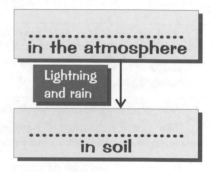

Nitrogen in the Soil

2) *Plants can use nitrates to make other compounds that contain nitrogen, such as DNA. The table below shows the chemical formulae of some compounds found in plants.*

Compound	Formula
fat (tristearin)	$C_{57}H_{110}O_6$
amino acid (glycine)	$C_2H_5O_2N$
carbohydrate (glucose)	$C_6H_{12}O_6$

a) How do *nitrates* get into the plant?

b) Which of the substances in the table would a plant *need* nitrates to make? What is then *made* from this substance?

c) Why are *DNA* and the *substances* named in your answer to part b) needed by plants?

d) When an animal feeds on a plant, in general what happens to the *nitrogen compounds* from the plant? What *use* does the animal make of them?

e) *Add* labelled *arrows* and *boxes* to your nitrogen cycle to show uptake of nitrates by plants, and feeding by animals.

3) *Nitrogen-fixing bacteria in the soil are able to convert gaseous nitrogen into nitrates in the soil. However, they are also found in root nodules of certain types of plants.*

a) Which type of plant has root *nodules*? *Give two examples* of this type of plant.

b) What is the *advantage* to plants of having root nodules?

c) *The grass near clover is often much more lush than grass further away. Suggest a reason why.*

d) *Scientists have been experimenting with root nodules to see if they can get them to stay on the roots of wheat plants.* Why should they want to do this? What *benefits* would there be in having wheat plants with root nodules?

e) *Add two labelled arrows* to your nitrogen cycle diagram to show nitrogen fixation by bacteria.

4) *Most processes discussed on this page are ones in which nitrogen from the atmosphere can be converted directly into nitrates.* Write a *summary* of them, including any organisms needed.

The Nitrogen Cycle

The Role that Microbes Play

5) Microbes can break down proteins in dead plants and animals. They can also break down proteins in faeces and urea in urine. In some cases, putrefying bacteria break down these compounds in the absence of oxygen to form terribly smelly amines (often with a "fishy" smell). Usually, microbes break down proteins and urea to form ammonia and ammonium compounds.

a) What is the name given to _bacteria_ which break down dead material?

b) Ammonia is a gas with a very distinctive smell, often experienced in public toilets and babies' nappies. Why should _ammonia_ be found in these places?

c) Ammonia dissolves easily in water to produce a solution with a pH of about 9. Ammonia solution can be used as a fertiliser. Suggest _two problems_ associated with doing this.

d) Fertiliser manufacturers usually convert ammonia into nitric acid, and then react the two together to make ammonium nitrate, which is a solid at room temperature and water-soluble. Why do fertiliser manufacturers mostly supply _ammonium nitrate_ rather than ammonia?

e) Nitrifying bacteria in the soil convert ammonia into nitrates. What _use_ are nitrates to plants?

f) The _diagram_ on the right represents part of the nitrogen cycle. _Copy it_, filling in the missing words. _Leave space_ for some more processes.

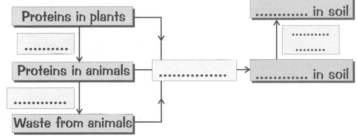

Denitrifying Bacteria

6) Denitrifying bacteria in the soil can convert nitrates in the soil into nitrogen gas.

a) _Add_ a labelled arrow and box to your nitrogen cycle to show the action of denitrifying bacteria.

b) _Add_ another labelled arrow to show the action of nitrogen-fixing bacteria in the soil. _Add_ a labelled arrow to show how nitrates get into plants.

c) Write a summary of the role of microbes in the nitrogen cycle. _Name_ each type of bacterium, what it _does_ and where it is _found_.

d) What could happen if denitrifying bacteria were _more active_ than decomposers, nitrogen-fixing bacteria and nitrifying bacteria? Would it matter if they were _less active_?

7) a) Why do farmers often plough plant remains _back into the soil_ after harvesting their crops?

b) It used to be common for the stubble (plant remains) to be burnt before ploughing. Would this make any _difference_ to the amount of _nitrogen_ compounds returned to the soil compared to just ploughing? Would it make any difference to the amount of _carbon_ compounds returned to the soil? _Suggest why_ farmers would want to burn stubble.

8) _Draw_ up a table with the headings shown on the right. _Complete_ your table to show the _processes_ that convert nitrogen into nitrates, those that convert ammonia and ammonium compounds into nitrates, and those that convert nitrates into nitrogen again.

nitrogen → nitrates	ammonia → nitrates	nitrates → nitrogen

Top Tips: The nitrogen cycle _is_ harder than the carbon cycle, and it's easy to get confused by the different microbes involved. You need to understand it if you are after a good grade, so go through it _carefully_ step by step. You won't be expected to draw the whole nitrogen cycle, but you _will_ have to _complete_, _label_ and _interpret_ one that they've drawn. Remember, you have to explain what happens to the nitrogen in each stage. Learn and enjoy.

1) a) Identify the types of microbe shown in the diagrams.

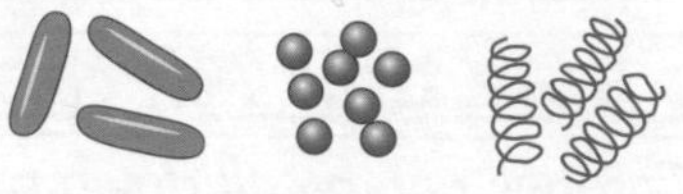

        Microbe in (i) ....
                                 (1 mark)

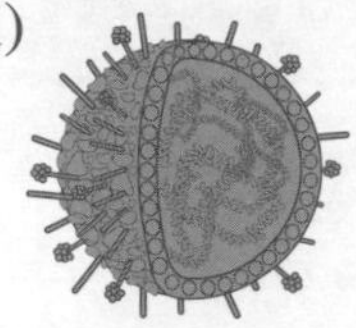

        Microbes in (ii) ....
                                 (1 mark)

i)

ii)

b) Describe how the skin and breathing organs defend the body against the entry of microbes.

                                                                      (3 marks)

c) Explain why diseases are more likely to occur in poorer areas with overcrowded conditions.

                                                                      (3 marks)

d) Why do we feel ill when disease-causing bacteria or viruses enter our body?

                                                                      (3 marks)

2) Study the information about diphtheria, then answer the questions below.

Diphtheria is a highly infectious disease caused by a microbe called *Corynebacterium diphtheria*. It especially affects children, and causes damage to the breathing system. A harmless form of the diphtheria toxin called a toxoid was developed in 1921. It has been used to immunise children against diphtheria. From the late 1940s a combined vaccine called DPT (diphtheria-pertussis-tetanus) has been given to nearly all pre-school children. The graph on the right shows the relative number of cases of diphtheria each year since 1910.

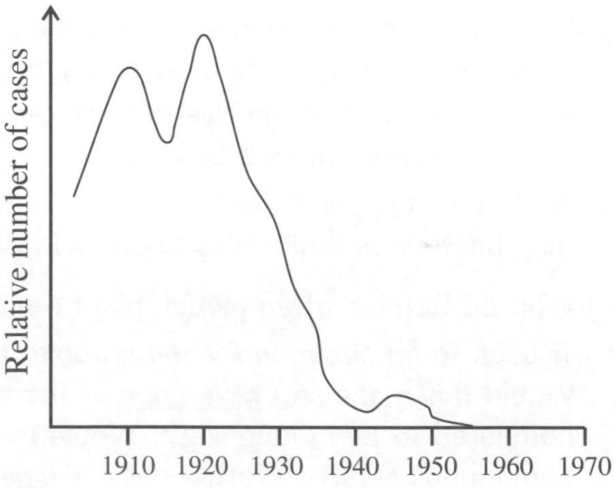

a) What **type** of microbe causes diphtheria?

                                                                      (1 mark)

b) Explain the changes in the number of cases of diphtheria since 1921.

                                                                      (3 marks)

3) The picture on the right shows how the fragrance moves away from a
woman wearing a lot of perfume.

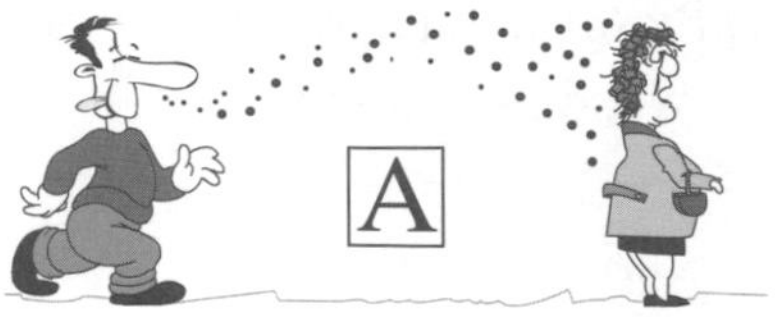

a) What is the name of this process?

....
(1 mark)

b) Give a definition of this process.

....
(1 mark)

c) Give **one** way to speed up this process.

....
(1 mark)

d) Leaf cells depend upon this process for gas exchange during photosynthesis. Name **one** gas
exchanged in this way.

Name of gas ....
(1 mark)

e) Give **two** features of leaves that allow them to exchange gases effectively using this process.

....
(2 marks)

f) What is meant by the term **concentration gradient**?

....
(1 mark)

4) A plant cell has a cellulose cell wall surrounding the cell membrane, and a vacuole inside
containing a solution of salts and other substances. The chart below shows what happens to the
cell in different environments.

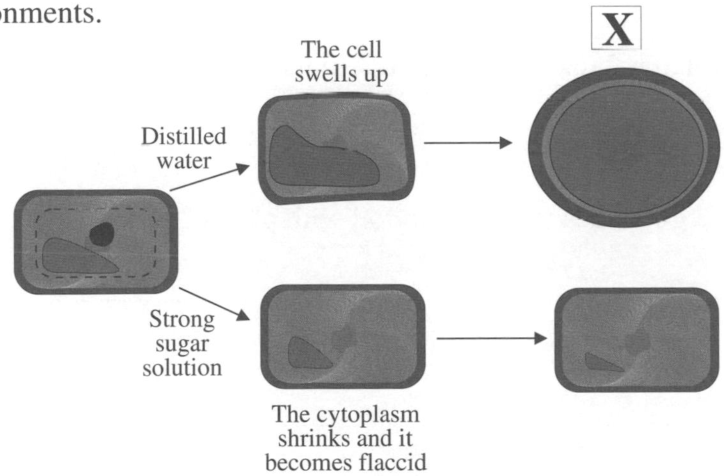

a) Explain what happens when the cell is put in distilled water. What word is used to describe the
cell at the point marked X on the chart?

....

....
(2 marks)

b) Explain what happens when the cell is put in strong sugar solution.

....

....
(2 marks)

SECTION SEVEN — TRIAL EXAM

5) a) Plants need carbon dioxide, water and light to perform photosynthesis. This is shown in the word equation below, but which two substances i) and ii) are missing?

carbon dioxide + water + light → i) .... + ii) ....
(2 marks)

b) The white parts of variegated leaves of plants have something missing. What is it and what is its function?

....
(1 mark)

c) If a variegated leaf were tested for starch, what would be the results and what would they mean?

....

....
(2 marks)

d) The following experiment was set up as shown to investigate the process of photosynthesis. The plant was left in a dark cupboard for 24 hours. It was thought that the plant soil should be covered with a plastic bag.

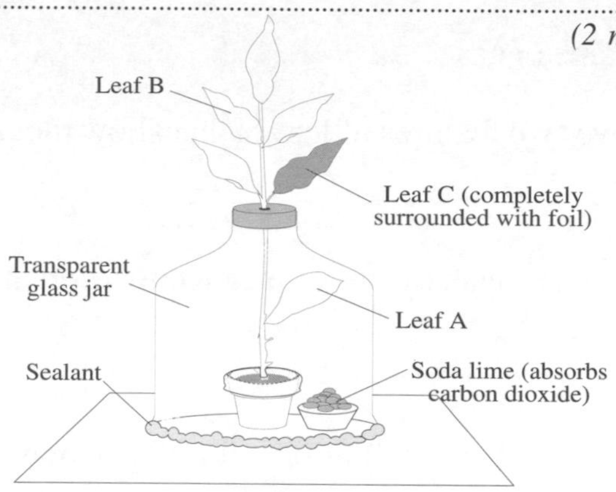

Leaf B

Leaf C (completely surrounded with foil)

Transparent glass jar

Leaf A

Sealant

Soda lime (absorbs carbon dioxide)

i) What job did the soda lime do?

....
(1 mark)

ii) Why was no starch found in discs tested from leaves **A** and **C**?

....
(1 mark)

iii) Why was it a good idea to cover the soil with plastic?

....
(1 mark)

iv) Leaf B was able to photosynthesise. Which gas could it produce?

....
(1 mark)

6) The graph shows the rate of photosynthesis of two different species of plant at different temperatures.

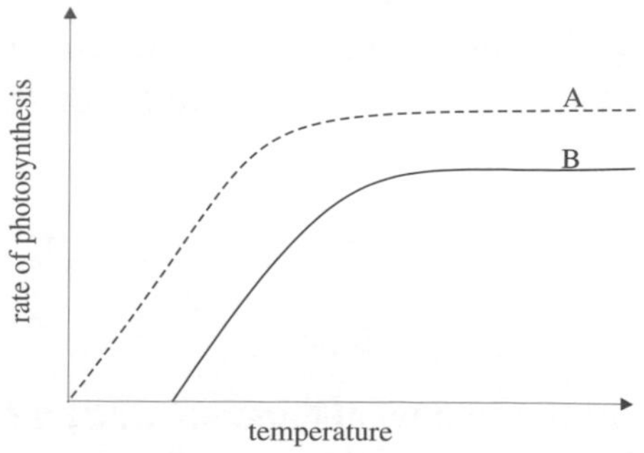

a) Explain the shape of the graph for plants **A** and **B**.

....

....
(2 marks)

rate of photosynthesis

A

B

temperature

b) Which plant, **A** or **B**, is more likely to grow in a cold climate and why?

....

....
(2 marks)

SECTION SEVEN — TRIAL EXAM

7) Children suffering from a lack of protein often have swollen bellies. The swelling is caused by water retention. This disease is called Kwashiorkor and is often seen in famine areas in Africa.
a) Give another way that a lack of protein can affect young children.

....
(1 mark)

b) Adult men and women also need to consume protein. Explain why.

....
(1 mark)

8) Our small intestine is approximately 8 metres long. Inside it are finger-like projections called villi (one is shown opposite).

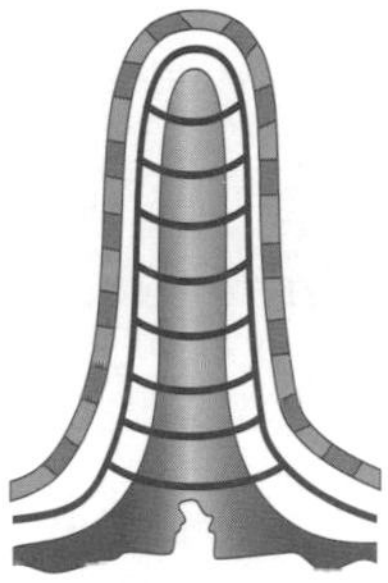

a) Give two functions of the small intestine.

....

....
(2 marks)

b) Why is it useful for the small intestine to be so long, and why is the internal surface covered in villi?

....
(2 marks)

c) The cross section of the intestine shows two types of muscle.
i) Give the names of the two types of muscle.

....
(2 marks)

ii) What is the function of these muscles?

....
(1 mark)

9) The diagram shows a model of how the small intestine works.

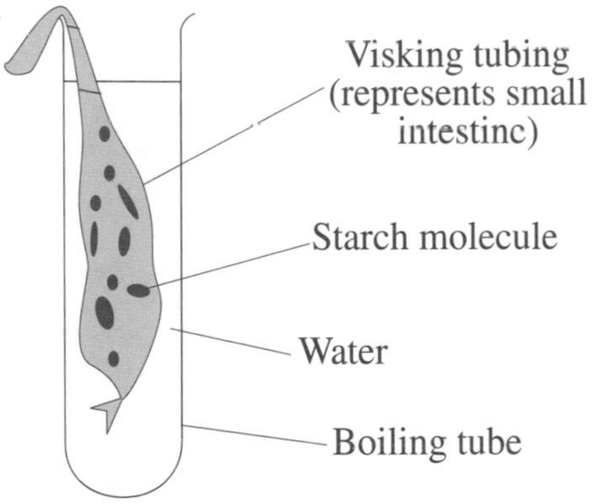

a) What fluid in the body does the water in the boiling tube represent?

....
(1 mark)

Visking tubing (represents small intestine)

Starch molecule

Water

Boiling tube

b) Why does starch stay inside the Visking tubing even though the tubing has pores in it?

....
(1 mark)

c) Carbohydrase (amylase) enzyme is added to the contents of the Visking tubing.
i) What substance will be produced from the starch?

....
(1 mark)

ii) This new substance is now found in the water in the boiling tube. By what process does this new substance move across the Visking tubing into the water?

....
(1 mark)

d) Describe a test for starch and state the results if starch is present.

....
(2 marks)

SECTION SEVEN — TRIAL EXAM

10) a) Label the diagram of the thorax on the right.   *(3 marks)*

b) What is the function of the breathing system?

....

....

....

....
                                              (2 marks)

c) Explain how the movement of the ribs and diaphragm causes air to move into the lungs as we inhale.

....

....

....

....
                                                                                          (4 marks)

d) Explain how the structure of the lungs allows gaseous exchange to take place effectively.

....

....

....
                                                                                          (4 marks)

e) Describe how the composition of exhaled air differs from that of inhaled air.

....

....
                                                                                          (3 marks)

11) a) What is the function of red blood cells?

....
                                                                                          (1 mark)

b) Explain how red blood cells are adapted for their function.

....

....
                                                                                          (2 marks)

c) Name **three** other main components of the blood, and briefly describe their functions.

....

....

....
                                                                                          (6 marks)

SECTION SEVEN — TRIAL EXAM

12) The following chart shows the menstrual cycle. Write in boxes B, C and D what happens to a
non-pregnant female between days 5 and 15, on or around day 15, and between days 15 and 28.

(3 marks)

DAY	1 2 3 4 5	6 7 8 9 10 11 12 13 14 15	16 17 18 19 20 21 22 23 24 25 26 27 28

↑ ↑ ↑ ↑

Menstruation lining breaks down and blood and waste products released	B	C	D

13) a) The hormones from various sources
control the menstrual cycle. Complete
parts i), ii), iii) and iv) on the diagram to
show the **name** of each hormone and its
source.   *(4 marks)*

brain

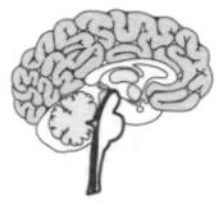

i) _____ gland

to ovaries   *to ovaries*

the hormone

ii) _____

is made to cause the egg
to mature and

iv) _____

hormone is made

iii) _____

is made to stimulate
the release of the egg

b) State why an injection of FSH may increase a woman's fertility.

....
(1 mark)

c) It is stated that the hormone oestrogen has a negative feedback control on another hormone.
Which hormone is this, and does oestrogen cause more or less of it to be made?

....
(1 mark)

14) The person in the diagram has smoked 20–25 cigarettes daily for
many years. When the person smokes the harmful gas **X** travels to the
lungs and the substance **Y** is deposited.

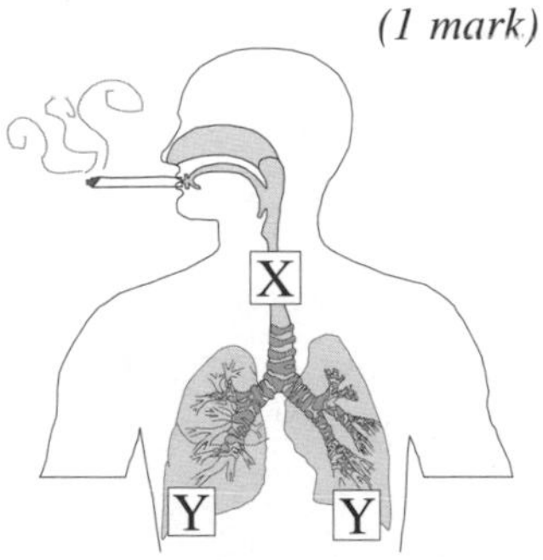

X

Y   Y

a) Give the name of gas X and what effect does it have on the blood?
Why should this put a strain on the heart?

....

....
(3 marks)

b) Give the name of substance **Y** and why does it cause breathing to become less efficient?

....

....
(2 mark)

c) Name a serious disease associated with smoking.

....
(1 mark)

SECTION SEVEN — TRIAL EXAM

15) The diagram on the right shows an aquatic food web.

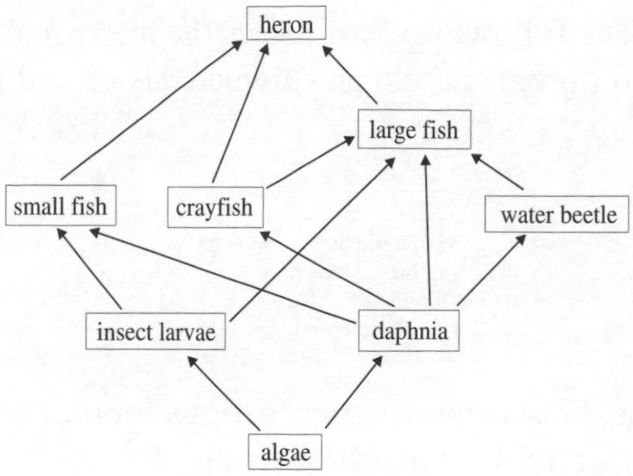

a) Name **two** prey of the large fish.

....

(2 marks)

b) Name **two** predators of the daphnia.

....

(2 marks)

c) The insect larvae mature, and the insects fly away. Explain what might happen to the population of daphnia as a result of this.

....

....

(2 marks)

d) i) Write down the longest food chain in the web.

....

(1 mark)

ii) In which direction does energy flow in this food chain?

....

(1 mark)

16) The diagram below shows the flow of energy through an ecosystem.

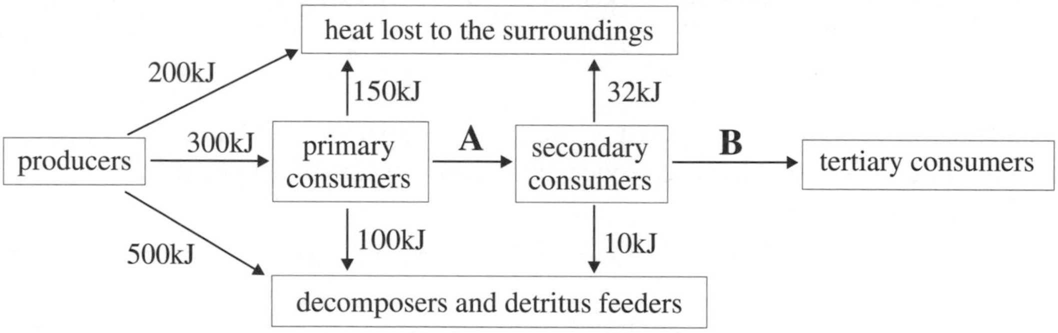

a) Work out the amounts of energy represented by **A** and **B**.

A .... kJ   *(1 mark)*   **B** .... kJ   *(1 mark)*

b) What percentage of the energy in the producers is lost as heat before reaching the tertiary consumer?

Percentage lost ....

(2 marks)

c) What is the name of the process in living organisms that produces the heat and, apart from producing heat, what else is this process used for by living organisms?

....

....

(1 mark)

d) Suggest, with reasons, **one** way in which food production could be made more efficient.

....

....

(1 mark)

SECTION SEVEN — TRIAL EXAM

17) a) In some areas of the world, many trees are being cut down. Give **two** reasons for this.

....

....
(2 marks)

b) Explain how deforestation will affect the amount of carbon dioxide in the atmosphere.

....

....
(2 marks)

c) Explain how deforestation and more rice paddy fields may lead to global warming.

....

....

....

....
(4 marks)

18) The pie chart shows the proportions of acid rain gases released in the UK recently.

a) Calculate the percentage contribution of road transport to the acid rain gases. Show your working out.

....

....

Percentage contribution = ... %
(1 mark)

b) Fossil fuels, such as oil, contain sulphur. What acid rain gas is produced when sulphur burns?

....
(1 mark)

c) Describe **two** effects of acid rain on the environment (exclude the effects in lakes).

....

....

....
(2 marks)

d) What will happen to the living things in a lake affected by acid rain?

....

....
(3 marks)

SECTION SEVEN — TRIAL EXAM

Lea
mar
bla

19) a) Give **two** examples of sense organs, and state the stimuli they respond to.

....

....
(2 marks)

b) Ashley touches a hot object with his finger. His finger quickly moves away from the heat. Explain how this happens.

....

....

....

....
(2 marks)

c) What are the functions of the spinal cord?

....

....
(2 marks)

d) Describe briefly how nerve impulses pass from one neurone to another.

....

....
(2 marks)

20) a) Label the diagram of the eye.   *(4 marks)*

b) Explain how the amount of light entering the eye is controlled .

....

....

....

....

....
(3 marks)

c) Explain how light from a distant object is focused onto the retina. Draw a ray diagram in the box below to illustrate your answer.
(5 marks)

....

....

....

....

SECTION SEVEN — TRIAL EXAM

21) The graph on the right shows the amount of
phytoplankton (tiny plants) in the sea during the year.

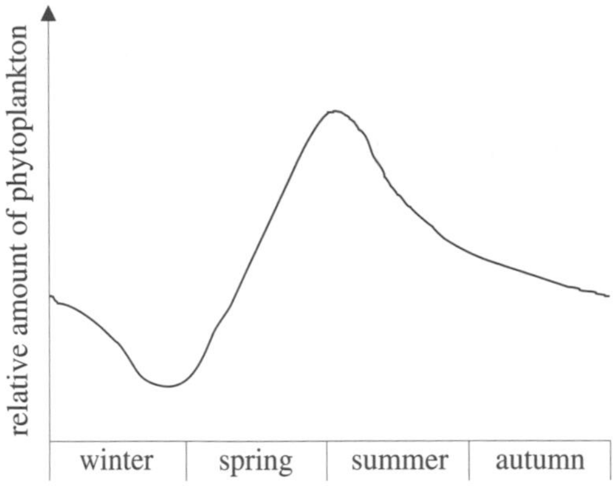

a) Suggest two reasons why the amount of
phytoplankton is higher in summer than it is
in the winter.

....

....

....
(2 marks)

Zooplankton are tiny sea animals that feed on the phytoplankton.

b) i) Draw a labelled line on the graph (in pencil) to show how you expect the population of
zooplankton to change during the year.   *(1 mark)*
ii) Explain briefly why you drew your line the way that you did.

....

....
(2 marks)

22) The graph on the right shows the changes in
a population of insect-eating birds in a wood
near some farmland.

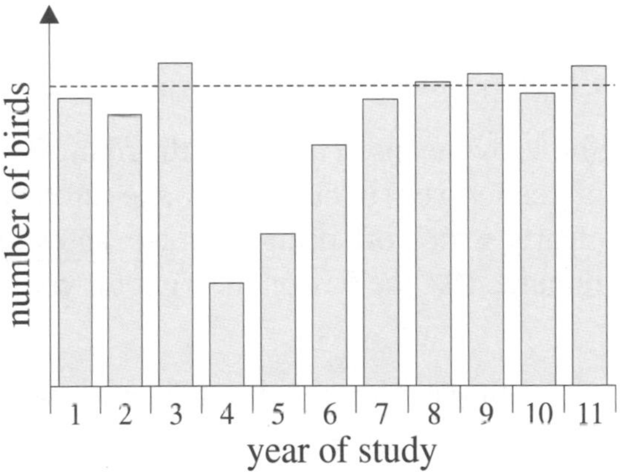

a) Why does the population of birds never reach
very far above the number indicated by the
dotted line?

....

....

....
(1 mark)

In the Spring of year 4, the farmer sprayed crops next to the woodland with insecticide.

b) i) What is an insecticide?

....
(1 mark)
ii) Explain how the use of the insecticide might have affected the population of birds.

....

....
(2 marks)
iii) Give **two** other possible reasons why the number of birds fell between years 3 and 4.

....

....
(2 marks)

SECTION SEVEN — TRIAL EXAM

Le
mar
bla

154

23) The diagram on the right shows a cell.
   a) Name the structures labelled (a) and (b).

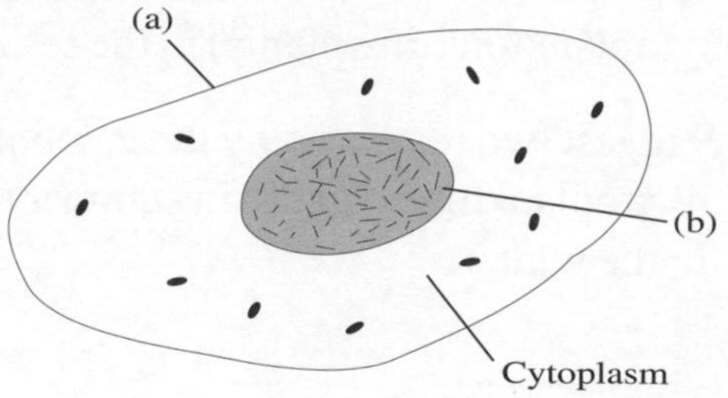

   Structure (a) ....
   (1 mark)

   Structure (b) ....
   (1 mark)

   (a)

   (b)

   Cytoplasm

   b) Which part of the cell, the cytoplasm or (b), contains genetic information?

   ....
   (1 mark)

   c) What is the chemical that carries the genetic information in animal and plant cells?

   ....
   (1 mark)

   d) The chemical named in c) is organised into certain structures in the cell. What are these?

   ....
   (1 mark)

   e) What is a **gene**?

   ....
   (1 mark)

24) a) In humans, which sex chromosomes are found in ova (eggs), and which are found in sperm?

   Chromosomes in ova .... Chromosomes in sperm ....
   (1 mark)

   b) Show, by means of a genetic diagram, the inheritance
      of gender (sex) in humans. Make sure you identify
      clearly which offspring are male, and which are
      female. Use the box on the right for your answer.
      (3 marks)

25) Cystic fibrosis is an inherited disorder, which affects
    the digestive and breathing systems. It is caused by a
    recessive allele of a gene. The normal allele can be
    shown as **F**, and the recessive allele as **f**.

   a) In a family, both parents have the genotype **Ff**.
      State whether the parents are homozygous or
      heterozygous for the gene, and whether they will
      have the cystic fibrosis disorder.

   ....

   ....
   (2 marks)

   b) Complete the genetic diagram on the right to
      show the inheritance of the disorder in the
      family. Underline any offspring who will
      suffer from the disorder.   *(4 marks)*

   | Parents | Ff | Ff |

   Gametes

   Offspring

SECTION SEVEN — TRIAL EXAM

26) a) Name the parts labelled A, B and C on the diagram opposite, which shows how the kidneys
are supplied with blood and what the waste liquid is excreted through.

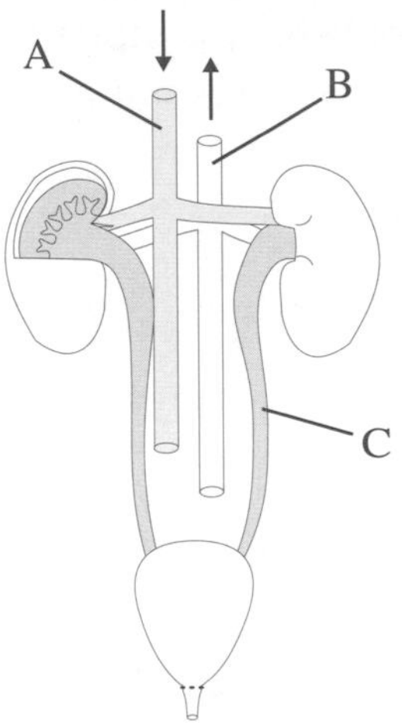

A ....

B ....

C ....
(3 marks)

b) The diagram of the kidney tubule shows how substances are removed
from the blood, some substances are returned to the blood, and others
leave the body in a liquid waste.

i) Name the process which squeezes liquid out of the
blood under pressure (as at (1) on the diagram).

....
(1 mark)

ii) Name the process by which substances are returned
to the blood (as at (2) on the diagram).

....
(1 mark)

iii) Name one substance in the waste liquid (as at (3) on
the diagram).

....
(1 mark)

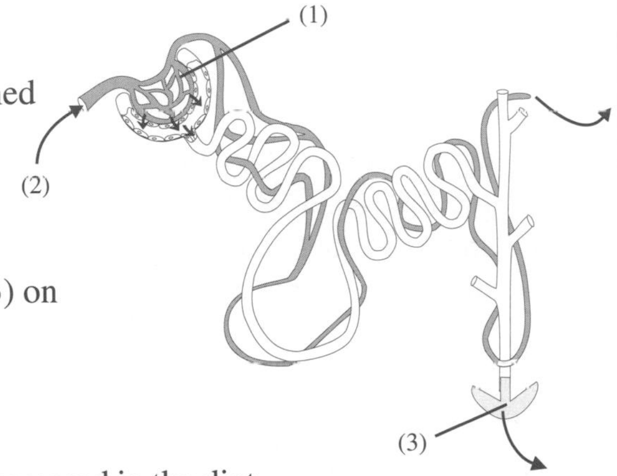

c) Urea contains nitrogen. Which nutrient should be decreased in the diet
if smaller amounts of urea are to be produced?

....
(1 mark)

27) Anti-diuretic hormone (ADH) from the pituitary gland controls the water content of the blood by
affecting the kidney tubules. Complete the flow chart below to show this mechanism .
(4 marks)

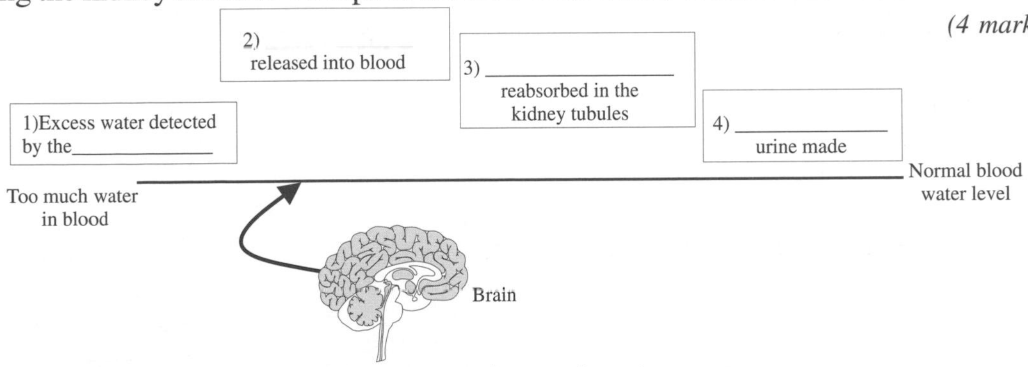

2) _____
released into blood

3) _____
reabsorbed in the
kidney tubules

1)Excess water detected
by the_____

4) _____
urine made

Normal blood
water level

Too much water
in blood

Brain

28) Homeostasis is the maintenance of a constant internal environment.
a) Name a substance, apart from water and waste products, which needs to be controlled in order
to maintain a constant internal environment.

....
(1 mark)

b) Name **two** hormones produced by the pancreas which control the level of glucose.

....
(1 mark)

c) Which organs in the body are involved in temperature control?

....
(3 marks)

SECTION SEVEN — TRIAL EXAM

Lea
marg
blan

29) There are two types of cell division, mitosis and meiosis.

  a) What is mitosis? Where in the body does mitosis occur? Give one example of a process that requires mitosis.

....

....

....

(3 marks)

  b) What is meiosis? Where in the body does meiosis occur? What type of cells are produced as a result of meiosis.

....

....

....

(3 marks)

30) The diagram shows some processes in reproduction. Answer the questions using using the words below (they can be used more than once, or not at all).

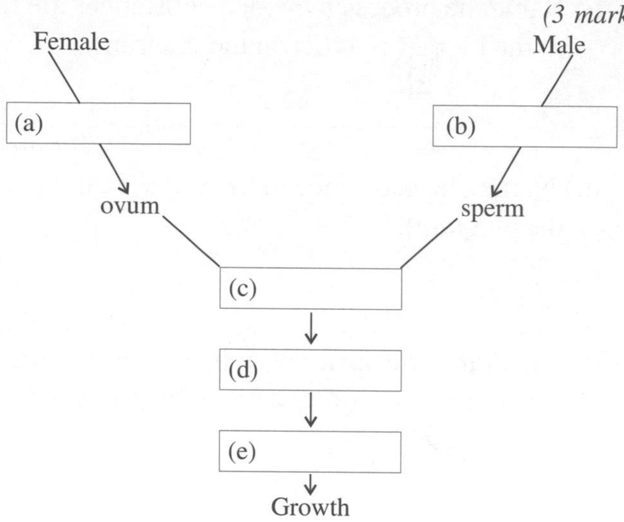

Female   Male

(a)   (b)

ovum   sperm

(c)

(d)

(e)

Growth

  Word list:
    mitosis, fertilisation, meiosis,
    gamete, haploid, diploid,
    fractionalise, zygote.

  a) Name of process (a) ....   b) Name of process (b)...

  c) Name of process (c) ....   d) Name of cell (d)...

  e) Name of process (e) ....

(5 marks)

31) This is a cell from a fruit fly.

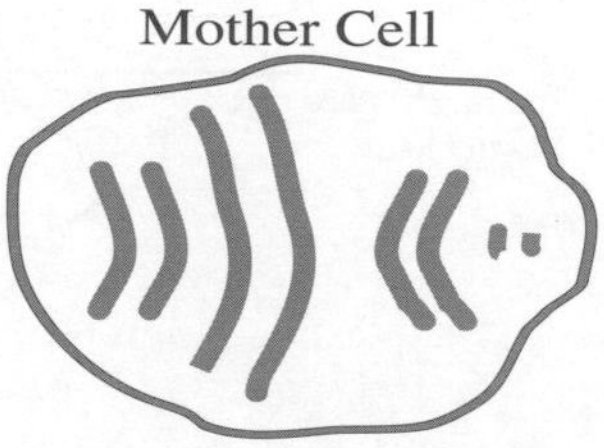

Mother Cell

  a) This cell has the full complement of chromosomes. What is the term for this?

....

(1 mark)

  b) Complete the diagram to the right to show the chromosomes in a daughter cell produced after the cell has divided to produce sex cells.   *(1 mark)*

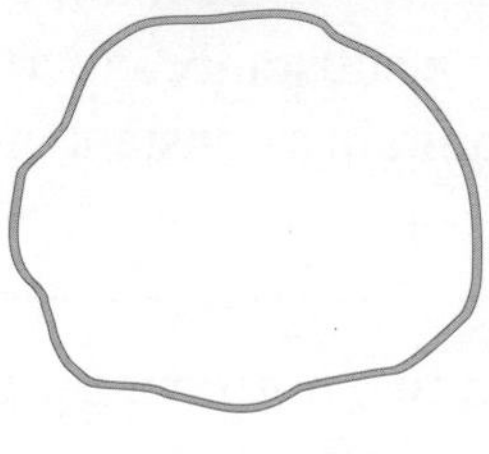

  c) How many sex cells are produced by this type of cell division?

....

(1 mark)

  d) Why are the chromosome numbers different in the mother cell and the sex cell?

....

(2 marks)

SECTION SEVEN — TRIAL EXAM